STUDY GUIDE

Wish You Well

David Baldacci

WITH CONNECTIONS

HOLT, RINEHART AND WINSTON

A Harcourt Education Company

Austin • Orlando • Chicago • New York • Toronto • London • San Diego

Staff Credits

Managing Editor: Marie Price

Assistant Managing Editor: Michael Neibergall

Executive Editor: Katie Vignery

Book Editor: Roger Boylan, Thomas Browne

Editorial Staff: *Editorial Operations Supervisor,* Lori De La Garza; *Senior Editorial Coordinator,* Janet Riley; *Copyediting Supervisor,* Mary Malone; *Copyeditors,* Christine Altgelt, Joel Bourgeois, Liz Dickson, Emily Force, Julie Hill, Julia Hu, Jennifer Kirkland, Millicent Ondras, Dennis Scharnberg; *Editorial Coordinators,* Betty Gabriel, Brian Kachmar, Jennifer Renteria; *Word Processing Supervisor,* Margaret Sanchez; *Word Processors,* Casey Kelly, Joie Pickett

Permissions: Catherine Paré, Carrie Jones

Design: *Design Director,* Joe Melomo; *Art Buyer Supervisor,* Elaine Tate

Prepress Production: Beth Prevelige, Gene Rumann, Carol Trammell

Manufacturing Coordinator: Shirley Cantrell

Electronic Publishing: *Project Team Leaders,* Christopher Lucas, Nanda Patel; *Specialists,* Ellen Kennedy, Patricia Zepeda

ISBN 0-03-068009-3

345678 085 09 08 07 06 05

TABLE *of* CONTENTS

Using This Study Guide

Approaching the Novel

The successful study of a novel often depends on students' enthusiasm, curiosity, and openness. The ideas in **Introducing the Novel** will help you create such a climate for your class. Background information in **About the Writer** and **About the Novel** can also be used to pique students' interest.

Reading and Responding to the Novel

Making Meanings questions are designed for both individual response and group or class discussion. They range from personal response to high-level critical thinking.

Reading Strategies worksheets contain graphic organizers. They help students explore techniques that enhance both comprehension and literary analysis. Many worksheets are appropriate for more than one set of chapters.

Novel Notes provide high-interest information relating to historical, cultural, literary, and other elements of the novel. The **Investigate** questions and **Reader's Log** ideas guide students to further research and consideration.

Choices suggest a wide variety of activities for exploring different aspects of the novel, either individually or collaboratively. The results may be included in a portfolio or used as springboards for larger projects.

Glossary and Vocabulary (1) clarifies allusions and other references and (2) provides definitions students may refer to as they read. The **Vocabulary Worksheets** activities are based on the Vocabulary Words.

Reader's Log, Double-Entry Journal, and **Group Discussion Log** model formats and spark ideas for responding to the novel. These pages are designed to be a resource for independent reading as well.

Responding to the Novel as a Whole

The following features provide options for culminating activities that can be used in whole-class, small-group, or independent-study situations.

Novel Review provides a format for summarizing and integrating the major literary elements.

Novel Projects suggest multiple options for culminating activities. **Writing About the Novel, Cross-Curricular Connections,** and **Multimedia and Internet Connections** propose project options that extend the text into other genres, content areas, and environments.

Responding to the Connections

Making Meanings questions in **Exploring the Connections** facilitate discussion of the additional readings in the HRW LIBRARY edition of this novel.

This Study Guide is intended to

- *provide maximum versatility and flexibility*
- *serve as a ready resource for background information on both the author and the book*
- *act as a catalyst for discussion, analysis, interpretation, activities, and further research*
- *provide reproducible masters that can be used for either individual or collaborative work, including discussions and projects*
- *provide multiple options for evaluating students' progress through the novel and the Connections*

Literary Elements

- plot structure
- major themes
- characterization
- setting
- point of view
- symbolism, irony, and other elements appropriate to the title

Making Meanings Reproducible Masters

- First Thoughts
- Shaping Interpretations
- Connecting with the Text
- Extending the Text
- Challenging the Text

A **Reading Check** focuses on review and comprehension.

The Worksheets Reproducible Masters

- Reading Strategies Worksheets
- Literary Elements Worksheets
- Vocabulary Worksheets

Reaching All Students

Because the questions and activities in this Study Guide are in the form of reproducible masters, labels indicating the targeted types of learners have been omitted.

Most classrooms include students from a variety of backgrounds and with a range of learning styles. The questions and activities in this Study Guide have been developed to meet diverse student interests, abilities, and learning styles. Of course, students are full of surprises, and a question or activity that is challenging to an advanced student can also be handled successfully by students who are less proficient readers. The interest level, flexibility, and variety of these questions and activities make them appropriate for a range of students.

Struggling Readers and Students with Limited English Proficiency: The **Making Meanings** questions, the **Choices** activities, and the **Reading Strategies** worksheets all provide opportunities for students to check their understanding of the text and to review their reading. The **Novel Projects** ideas are designed for a range of student abilities and learning styles. Both questions and activities motivate and encourage students to make connections to their own interests and experiences. The **Vocabulary Worksheets** can be used to facilitate language acquisition. **Dialogue Journals,** with you the teacher or with more advanced students as respondents, can be especially helpful to these students.

Advanced Students: The writing opportunity suggested with the **Making Meanings** questions and the additional research suggestions in **Novel Notes** should offer a challenge to these students. The **Choices** and **Novel Projects** activities can be taken to advanced levels. **Dialogue Journals** allow advanced students to act as mentors or to engage each other intellectually.

Auditory Learners: A range of suggestions in this Study Guide targets students who respond particularly well to auditory stimuli: making and listening to audiotapes and engaging in class discussion, role-playing, debate, oral reading, and oral presentation. See **Making Meanings** questions, **Choices,** and **Novel Projects** options (especially **Cross-Curricular Connections** and **Multimedia and Internet Connections**).

Visual/Spatial Learners: Students are guided to create visual representations of text scenes and concepts and to analyze films or videos in **Choices** and in **Novel Projects.** The **Reading Strategies** and **Literary Elements Worksheets** utilize graphic organizers as a way to both assimilate and express information.

Tactile/Kinesthetic Learners: The numerous interactive, hands-on, and problem-solving projects are designed to encourage the involvement of students motivated by action and movement. The projects also provide an opportunity for **interpersonal learners** to connect with others through novel-related tasks. The **Group Discussion Log** will help students track the significant points of their interactions.

Verbal Learners: For students who naturally connect to the written and spoken word, the **Reader's Logs** and **Dialogue Journals** will have particular appeal. This Study Guide offers numerous writing opportunities: See **Making Meanings, Choices, Novel Notes,** and **Writing About the Novel** in **Novel Projects.** These options should also be attractive to **intrapersonal learners.**

Assessment Options

Perhaps the most important goal of assessment is to provide feedback on the effectiveness of instructional strategies. As you monitor the degree to which your students understand and engage with the novel, you will naturally adjust the frequency and ratio of class to small-group and verbal to nonverbal activities, as well as the extent to which direct teaching of reading strategies, literary elements, or vocabulary is appropriate to your students' needs.

If you are in an environment where **portfolios** contain only carefully chosen samples of students' writing, you may want to introduce a second, "working," portfolio and negotiate grades with students after examining all or selected items from this portfolio.

The features in this Study Guide are designed to facilitate a variety of assessment techniques.

Reader's Logs and Double-Entry Journals can be briefly reviewed and responded to (students may wish to indicate entries they would prefer to keep private). The logs and journals are an excellent measure of students' engagement with and understanding of the novel.

Group Discussion Log entries provide students with an opportunity for self-evaluation of their participation in both book discussions and project planning.

Making Meanings questions allow you to observe and evaluate a range of student responses. Those who have difficulty with literal and interpretive questions may respond more completely to **Connecting** and **Extending**. The **Writing Opportunity** provides you with the option of ongoing assessment: You can provide feedback to students' brief written responses to these prompts as they progress through the novel.

Reading Strategies Worksheets, Novel Review, and Literary Elements Worksheets lend themselves well to both quick assessment and students' self-evaluation. They can be completed collaboratively and the results shared with the class, or students can compare their individual responses in a small-group environment.

Choices activities and writing prompts offer all students the chance to successfully complete an activity, either individually or collaboratively, and share the results with the class. These items are ideal for peer evaluation and can help prepare students for presenting and evaluating larger projects at the completion of the novel unit.

Vocabulary Worksheets can be used as diagnostic tools or as part of a concluding test.

Novel Projects evaluations might be based on the degree of understanding of the novel demonstrated by the project. Students' presentations of their projects should be taken into account, and both self-evaluation and peer evaluation can enter into the overall assessment.

The **Test** is a traditional assessment tool in three parts: objective items, short-answer questions, and essay questions.

Questions for Self-evaluation and Goal Setting

- What are the three most important things I learned in my work with this novel?
- How will I follow up so that I remember them?
- What was the most difficult part of working with this novel?
- How did I deal with the difficulty, and what would I do differently?
- What two goals will I work toward in my reading, writing, group, and other work?
- What steps will I take to achieve those goals?

Items for a "Working" Portfolio

- reading records
- drafts of written work and project plans
- audio- and videotapes of presentations
- notes on discussions
- reminders of cooperative projects, such as planning and discussion notes
- artwork
- objects and mementos connected with themes and topics in the novel
- other evidence of engagement with the book

For help with establishing and maintaining portfolio assessment, examine the **Portfolio Management System** *in* ELEMENTS OF LITERATURE.

Answer Key

The Answer Key at the back of this guide is not intended to be definitive or to set up a right-wrong dichotomy. In questions that involve interpretation, however, students' responses should be defended by citations from the text.

More on Baldacci

"Baldacci, David." **Contemporary Authors,** Volume 187, pp. 12–14. Detroit: Gale Group, 2000. This article presents a detailed overview of Baldacci's work and a solid biographical background.

Also by Baldacci

Absolute Power. New York: Warner Books, 1996.

Total Control. New York: Warner Books, 1997.

The Winner. New York: Warner Books, 1997.

The Simple Truth. New York: Warner Books, 1998.

Saving Faith. New York: Warner Books, 1999.

Last Man Standing. New York: Warner Books, 2001.

A biography of David Baldacci appears in Wish You Well, *HRW Library Edition. You may wish to share this additional biographical information with your students.*

Although Baldacci seems to have appeared on the scene overnight with a best-selling novel, he has claimed in an interview that his overnight success actually took "eleven years and probably 10,000 discarded pages." Baldacci worked hard to become a writer and continues to work hard, particularly when it comes to research. "For me," says Baldacci, "doing my own research is essential to the writing process."

Of course Baldacci reads up on the subject he'll be writing about, but that's only a start. To make his stories more interesting and realistic, Baldacci talks to people one-on-one, finding out how they work and act. For a novel on the Supreme Court, Baldacci interviewed scholars who have studied the court, lawyers who have argued cases before the court, and people who have worked at the court. While researching the FBI's Hostage Rescue Team (HRT) for another book, Baldacci visited HRT's headquarters and spent time with HRT operators. Baldacci even gets hands-on: He's tried out night-vision equipment, learned to ride a horse, and fired machine guns—all in the name of book research.

Baldacci's hard work doesn't stop with matters related to his writing. He participates in numerous charitable organizations and sits on the boards of the Multiple Sclerosis Society and Virginia Blood Services. He has given workshops to children interested in creative writing, and has set up scholarships for students interested in the creative arts.

About the Novel

Wish You Well is set in the mountains of southwestern Virginia. Those mountains are part of the Appalachians, a mountain system that runs from Canada all the way into Alabama. The southern mountain region, commonly known as Appalachia, has long been viewed as a place apart from the rest of America, relatively untouched by modernization. Because of rough terrain that hindered the building of roads, portions of Appalachia had little contact with the outside world until the early twentieth century. As a result, Appalachian highlanders developed a unique culture with its own handicrafts, folklore, ballads, and customs. Unfortunately, Appalachia in general is often associated with poverty, and Appalachian Virginia in particular has a history of population pressure and low employment.

The southern United States had a fundamentally rural culture until almost the middle of the twentieth century, with most families making their living through farming. Only after World War II did the region begin to shift to a primarily urban and industrial way of life. Before that time, even the methods of farming were resistant to change, and mechanized farming was not widespread until the forties, when balers, combines, tractors, mechanical cotton pickers, and sophisticated machinery began to replace humans and mules. These pre-World War II farms were small, too: In 1930, 80 percent of the farms in the Southeast were under 100 acres. A large number of these farms were subsistence farms, meaning that they did not raise crops primarily for sale, but for survival. Although Virginia was not as mired in subsistence farming as were other southern states, it did have large numbers of these small farms, especially in the mountain counties. These small farms were remarkably resistant to the pressures of economic recessions and depressions, simply because it was hardly possible for them to make less money than they already made.

Commercial production of coal in southwestern Virginia began in 1881, providing a much-needed source of employment for the overpopulated area. Thousands found jobs in mining and related activities. Nonetheless, the wages were fairly low, and miners' homes were often in a state of ill repair, overcrowded, and lacking running water. In the twentieth century, the shrinking coal market led to fewer working days for miners and serious unemployment problems in the region.

In *Wish You Well,* Baldacci takes the historical elements of subsistence farming and coal mining in southwestern Virginia and puts them together to create drama.

Special Considerations

Possible sensitive issues in this novel include a character with the nickname of Hell No, some mild profanity, and some ethnic slurs against African Americans and American Indians spoken by the antagonist, George Davis.

For Listening

Wish You Well. Time Warner Audiobooks, 2000. An unabridged, seven-cassette recording of the book, read by Norma Lana.

Wish You Well. Time Warner Audiobooks, 2000. An abridged, four-cassette recording of the book, read by Kate Burton.

Wish You Well. Time Warner Audiobooks, 2000. An abridged, five-CD recording of the book, read by Kate Burton.

Sources of the Novel

Among his favorite writers Baldacci lists Harper Lee and Mark Twain, and these preferences show in *Wish You Well*. The book borrows situations and characters from Lee's *To Kill a Mockingbird* and Twain's *The Adventures of Huckleberry Finn*.

- The main plot line of *To Kill a Mockingbird* focuses on a young southern girl who watches a court case bring out the best and the worst in the people who live around her.
- The main character of *To Kill a Mockingbird,* Scout Finch, is a model for Lou Cardinal in many ways. Scout is a tomboy who is more than willing to get into schoolyard fistfights over insults. She, too, has lost a parent to death and spends much of her time playing and creating mischief with her brother and another boy.
- Atticus Finch, Scout's father, provides the prototype for Cotton Longfellow. Both are unfailingly moral and decent men who practice law. They both take on cases for poor people, accepting goods and services in lieu of cash payment. Most important, they both argue cases that end up pitting them against their neighbors.
- The title character of Mark Twain's *The Adventures of Huckleberry Finn* is a free-spirited, ragged-clothed young boy who comes and goes as he pleases. His appearance, diction, superstition, inherent goodness, and general attitude toward life are all mirrored in Diamond Skinner, the close friend of Lou and Oz Cardinal.

Literary Context

Baldacci's tale of a young girl coming to terms with hard-learned lessons of life falls into the genre of the *Bildungsroman*. The term is German for "novel of education," and a *Bildungsroman* typically deals with the personal development of a young person. The story ends on a positive note, although the protagonist may have experienced loss on the path to wisdom. The theme of personal development has a long tradition in folklore epic literature, but the first novel to develop this theme fully was German author Johann Wolfgang von Goethe's *Wilhelm Meisters Lehrjahre (Wilhelm Meister's Apprenticeship),* written in 1795–1796. The book became extremely influential, and is the classic example of *Bildungsroman*. One of the better-known English examples of the genre is Charles Dickens's *David Copperfield*.

Critical Responses

Critics have responded positively to Baldacci's move away from legal thrillers to a coming-of-age tale, praising the book's emotional appeal. *Publishers Weekly* remarks that the novel offers "bone-deep emotional truth," finds the characters "as real as readers' own kin," and concludes that "This novel has a huge heart." *Library Journal* calls the book "affecting," and calls attention to its "richly textured setting of south-western Virginia in the 1940s," while the *Richmond Times-Dispatch* calls the book "an uplifting gospel that speaks to the strength of family bonds."

Less agreement has been reached about Baldacci's writing style. The *Denver Post* admires "some wonderfully lyric prose" in *Wish You Well,* and the *Wichita Falls Times Record News* calls the book "a beautifully written tale," but *Booklist* has a different opinion:

> Unfortunately, his tale is marred by an over-wrought prose style. Nonetheless, if readers can overlook the writing style (and that's a big if), the story might appeal not only to the author's fans but also to readers of coming-of-age fiction.

The plotting of the book has also garnered some negative attention. *Booklist* again complains, remarking that the Cardinals' conflict with Southern Valley Coal and Gas "arises seemingly out of nowhere." Kelly Flynn of Amazon.com calls the plot "a trifle transparent." However, Flynn goes on to say, "neither reader nor character is the worse for it. After all, nostalgia is about remembering things one already knows."

The Novel at a Glance

Plot and Setting

Wish You Well takes place in the mountains of Virginia in the 1940s. The main character, Lou Cardinal, is a twelve-year-old girl whose father was killed and her mother incapacitated in a car crash. She, her brother, Oz, and her mother, Amanda, leave their home in New York City to live with Lou's great-grandmother Louisa on a primitive farm in Virginia. While there, Lou and Oz meet many colorful locals and learn to love the simple country life, all the while waiting for Amanda to recover. Eventually, the family becomes embroiled in a land dispute that pits them against their neighbors and the local coal-and-gas company. When Louisa has a stroke and enters a coma, the question of who controls her property is contested in court. Louisa dies, and the children's future seems uncertain. Their mother recovers miraculously just in the nick of time, saving the farm and the children.

Structure and Point of View

The novel has a standard structure: a **continuous narrative** broken into chapters. The book can be divided loosely into four sections. The first section introduces the main characters and establishes the setting. In the second section, the major conflicts are introduced. The conflicts intensify and the action increases in the third section. The fourth section unites the two main conflicts, brings them to a head, and resolves them. An epilogue at the end ties up loose ends and gives a glimpse into the main characters' futures.

The novel is written from the **third-person point of view.** For the most part, the story is told from the vantage point of the main character, Lou. However, some scenes are described for which Lou is not present.

Major Characters

Lou Cardinal, a twelve-year-old girl who wants to follow in the footsteps of her novelist father, finds her life suddenly changed by a car accident that kills her father and incapacitates her mother. Lou, her mother, and her brother move to the farm of her great-grandmother in the mountains of Virginia. Tough, smart, and skeptical, Lou learns to adapt to life on a primitive farm, and resists sentimentality regarding her mother's condition.

Oz Cardinal is Lou's seven-year-old brother. Although small for his age and more timid than Lou, Oz is fiercely loyal and has a warm, generous nature. He has great reserves of hope for his mother's recovery.

A **Reading Strategies** worksheet titled **Understanding Character** appears on page 29 of this Study Guide.

Amanda Cardinal is the mother of Oz and Lou. She has a special bond with Oz. In the car wreck that kills her husband, Amanda sustains injuries while protecting her children. For much of the book she is bedridden and unable to move or speak.

Louisa Mae Cardinal, the great-grandmother of Lou and Oz, takes in the children and their mother. She is a tall, strong-willed, fair-minded woman who runs her own farm on a mountain in Virginia.

Eugene is a man who has lived on Louisa's farm since he was orphaned as a young child.

Diamond is the nickname of Jimmy Skinner, a free-spirited boy who lives alone on the mountain. He befriends the Cardinal children and is involved in most of their adventures.

Cotton Longfellow, Louisa's lawyer, befriends the Cardinal family and reads regularly to Amanda. When Louisa's property is in dispute, Cotton works to defend the family's rights.

George Davis is a foul-tempered neighboring farmer who deals in illegal moonshine and starves his family despite his material success. He becomes involved in an attempt to wrest the Cardinal farm from the Cardinal family.

Themes

Hope and despair: Throughout the book, Lou and Oz struggle to maintain hope for their mother's recovery. Oz succumbs to despair less readily than Lou, but even his hopes wane from time to time. Their hope is constantly bolstered by Louisa, who encourages them in the rituals and gestures that help them maintain their faith. Toward the end of the book, when things seem most desperate, the children focus their hope on Louisa.

Children without parents: Many of the novel's characters lack parents. Lou and Oz, Eugene, Diamond, Jack Cardinal, and Billy Davis all lack parents either literally or practically. Some are orphaned, some abandoned, and some neglected, but all must find ways to go on without parental care and guidance. The Cardinal children find a substitute in Louisa; Diamond treasures his independence; and Billy Davis, a schoolmate of Lou's, lashes out against others. Other characters' treatment of these parentless children drives much of the plot: Louisa and Cotton work to help them, while Southern Valley Coal and Gas and George Davis work to take advantage of them.

A **Literary Elements** worksheet that focuses on **theme** appears on page 46 of this Study Guide.

Major Symbols

The wishing well symbolizes the children's hope for their mother's recovery, and later, their hope for Louisa's. The well demands a sacrifice of a cherished possession, calling to mind the sacrifices that people must make in order to get what is really important to them.

At first, **the land** on which the farm sits symbolizes life in the way it rewards and punishes seemingly at random. Later, the land comes to symbolize the Cardinal family, and their fight to retain the land is also a fight to preserve their family.

A **Literary Elements** worksheet that focuses on **symbol** appears on page 47 of this Study Guide.

Options

Engaging Issues

Although the action of *Wish You Well* takes place in the first half of the twentieth century, the issues the Cardinals and their friends face continue to be relevant. Prepare students for the novel by engaging them in aspects of these issues that might affect students' own lives.

Ask students to discuss in small groups both sides of each of these scenarios, come to a consensus, and present their conclusions to the class.

SCENARIOS

Maintaining Hope vs. Facing Reality

- A friend of yours has a younger sister who has entered a contest to win a trip to Paris. The chances of her winning are extremely slim. Your friend's sister has developed some superstitious habits—such as wearing a lucky ring and clicking her heels whenever the contest is mentioned—that she believes increase her chances of winning. Your friend is annoyed by his sister's superstition and wishes she would understand that such rituals will have no real effect on the outcome of the contest. On the other hand, the rituals keep his sister optimistic and give her a sense of control over her future. Should your friend reason with his sister and try to discourage her superstitious behavior, or should he tolerate this behavior, knowing that it comforts her?

Whose Sacrifice?

- An antique dining-room set is divided among various households in your family. An antique dealer has appraised the furniture and is willing to pay a very large sum for it; however, he wishes to buy only the complete set. If any pieces are missing, he will not buy. Your aunt, who has the table, is unwilling to give it up because of a profound sentimental attachment to it. The other members of your family are pressuring her to let go of it so that they can sell the lot and split the money. Your aunt wants the other members of your family to be able to enjoy the money, but the table has been with her all her life and has great meaning for her. What should your aunt do?

CLASS DISCUSSION

Primitive Accommodations

Ask students to imaging having to leave their homes and live on a farm on a mountaintop that has no electricity, no running water, no telephone, and no grocery stores within reach. Have the students discuss what they would have to do to provide themselves with food, sanitation, communication, and entertainment. What main differences would there be in their lives?

PREDICTING

Sibling Study

Ask students to think about the different ways that siblings interact with each other: fighting, supporting, ignoring, etc. Then, read aloud to them the second through fourth paragraphs of the novel. Discuss the descriptions of Lou and Oz, and elicit from students words that, to them, describe Lou's and Oz's personalities. Next, invite students to do the following:

- In their Reader's Logs, have students write a paragraph describing how they predict the relationship between Lou and Oz will be represented in the novel. Ask them to consider the following points: Who is more likely to start an argument, and who is more likely to make up? How will the two interact with each other when things are normal? How will they interact when they encounter a crisis?

Plot Synopsis and Literary Elements

Chapters 1–10

Plot Synopsis

Twelve-year-old Lou Cardinal lives with her family in New York City in the 1940s, where her father, Jack, is a critically acclaimed writer with little commercial success. Lou is always writing stories, and hopes to become a professional writer like her father. One day as Jack drives the family home from a picnic, he and Lou's mother, Amanda, argue. Distracted by the argument, Jack narrowly misses a stalled car and swerves off the road. The accident kills Jack and incapacitates Amanda. The children, Lou and her brother Oz, are unhurt. Amanda's condition is odd, in that even after she is physically healed, and can eat and drink with assistance, she cannot move or speak. Low on money and needing someone to care for Amanda, the family moves to the Virginia mountain farm of Jack's grandmother, Louisa Mae Cardinal, after whom Lou was named.

On the train trip to Virginia, Oz attempts to cure his mother with a magic necklace, and Lou scolds him for being superstitious. Lou further claims that their mother deserves her fate for causing the car accident. At the train station Virginia, the children are met by a silent African American man who drives them to their great-grandmother's house as Amanda rides ahead in an ambulance. On the way, they pick up a red-headed local boy named Jimmy Skinner, who prefers to be called Diamond. When Diamond ridicules Oz for carrying a teddy bear, Lou decides she does not like the new boy. He hops off to do some fishing, and they go along their way. Eventually the driver gets up enough courage to tell the children that his name is Eugene and that their great-grandmother took him in when he was a child.

The children arrive at their new home to discover that it is on a large farm with cows, horses, pigs, and mules, and without electricity, telephone, or running water. The house is old and in need of some maintenance, but neat and clean. Louisa Mae Cardinal is a tall, straight, eighty-year-old woman whose sternness frightens Oz but gives Lou the impression that great kindness lies behind it. Amanda is put in a bright, comfortable room on the first floor, and Lou is given the second-floor room that was her father's when he was a child and contains his old desk. Louisa explains to Lou and Oz that they will be rising at five o'clock in the morning, performing chores, and then either walking to school or riding a horse there. When Oz uses his magic necklace on Amanda, Lou storms out of the room, but Louisa encourages him in his hope. Diamond shows up with several fish, which become dinner. While the group eats, Diamond tells them that strangers have been exploring local farmers' property. Louisa tells him to keep an eye on the situation. As the conversation takes another turn, Lou discovers that Eugene's parents died when he was a child.

Literary Elements

Plot: Chapters 1–10 set the stage for the story, introducing most of the main characters, the setting, and the characters' basic situation. The main **internal conflict** of the book is revealed as the struggle within Lou between her resentment of her mother and her desire for her mother to recover.

Themes

Hope and despair: On the train to Virginia, Oz begins his rituals of hope for his mother's recovery, using his supposedly magic necklace in an attempt to revive her. He will continue his rituals at the farm, with Louisa's encouragement. Lou, on the other hand, wants nothing to do with Oz's rituals, and has given up hope, embracing instead bitterness and blame. These two competing attitudes will inform the way the children react to their situation throughout the novel.

Children without parents: Lou and Oz have lost both their parents in a car accident: one to death, the other to incapacity. They soon meet up with

Diamond, a boy who appears to have no authority figures in his life. The children discover later that Eugene, a man who lives on the farm with them, was orphaned when he was very young. People who have lost parents early and learned to live without them are a recurring element in the novel.

Setting: The setting for the rest of the novel is established in these chapters. The rugged, mountainous, primitive farm without electricity, telephone, or running water will rule much of the characters' lives. Although the book makes forays into the small town of Dickens from time to time, its focus remains the farm and the countryside surrounding it.

Symbol: Oz's **necklace** is a symbol of his faith and hope that his mother will recover. When it is taken from him by the nurse on the train, Lou steals it back for him. Even though Lou doesn't share Oz's hope in

their mother's recovery, she often bolsters him when he is feeling despondent. Her returning the necklace to him is symbolic of her willingness to support him without sharing his belief.

Characterization: Physical description is a strong indicator of character. For example, Diamond is unkempt, wearing dirty overalls, and having his hair in "crazy-angled cowlicks," indicating his wild, free-spirited nature. Lou's first impression of Louisa is of a lean, tall, strong woman, "statue-like in her majesty." Other physical indicators of character are that Oz sucks his thumb and carries a teddy bear, signaling his immaturity and dependence, and that Eugene walks with a limp, bringing to mind the hardships he has endured and continues to endure.

Foreshadowing: Diamond's mention of strange men exploring on local farmers' land heralds a later conflict.

Chapters 11–20

Plot Synopsis

Diamond and the two Cardinal children begin to develop a friendship. He gives Oz a lucky rabbit's foot, and allows him to throw a ball for Diamond's dog, Jeb, to chase. Diamond leads the other two in a search for a haunted well. As they search, they run across George Davis, a local farmer, who threatens them with a shotgun. When Davis is distracted by the scream of a mountain lion, the children run off. Diamond explains that Davis keeps a still in the area and doesn't want anyone to discover it. When they get to the well, Diamond reveals that two star-crossed lovers killed themselves by jumping into the well, and in addition to haunting the place, will grant wishes if the wisher will leave the ghosts a prized possession.

The next day, the children meet Cotton Longfellow, Louisa's lawyer. Cotton relays the news that the men who have been exploring in the area seem to be looking for oil. Before he leaves, Cotton offers to

come back and read to Amanda on a regular basis. A few days later, the children witness the birth of a new calf. Oz runs in to tell Amanda about it, but Lou claims that telling her is futile. In response, Louisa gives the girl a stack of letters that Amanda had sent her over the years. The next morning, Lou gets up extra early to massage and exercise her mother's limbs, but won't reveal to Louisa whether she's read any of the letters. That day the children attend their new school for the first time. The school has one room and one teacher, Estelle McCoy. When the children arrive, they are immediately labeled Yankees by the other children and have a confrontation with George Davis's son Billy. After school, Louisa beats Billy in a fight. Cotton Longfellow arrives at the house that afternoon and commiserates, revealing that he is also a Yankee and a descendent of the poet Henry Wadsworth Longfellow. His plan to read one of Jack Cardinal's books to Amanda makes Oz hopeful but offends Lou. At Louisa's suggestion, he instead reads some of the letters that Jack sent Louisa. Lou overhears the reading and is touched, but is also angered that it has no visible effect on Amanda.

Late one night, Oz sneaks out of the house to leave his teddy bear at the wishing well and wish for his mother's recovery. Lou, who has followed him in secret, waits until he leaves and then makes the same wish, offering a picture of herself and Amanda.

Time passes, and the children become more adept at farm work, getting the fields plowed and ready for seed. They are also beginning to fit in at school, but their chief friend remains Diamond, who one Saturday takes them to his tree house and shows them his various treasures, including his prized possession, a lump of coal in the center of which he is sure a diamond resides. The children come up with a plan to go to the nearby town of Dickens. After negotiating Diamond's dangerous shortcut, they arrive in town and see *The Wizard of Oz,* the first movie Diamond has ever seen. They run into Cotton Longfellow, who shows them the courthouse and his office, where Diamond hears a voice over the telephone for the first time. He shows them his house, in which he has a huge collection of books, including everything Jack Cardinal ever published. Cotton then takes everyone shopping. Lou buys gifts for everyone, and Oz buys a hairbrush for Amanda. When they get home, Lou shows him how to brush Amanda's hair properly. A few nights later, Cotton shows up at dinner to tell Diamond that a prank was pulled on the coal mine superintendent, and Diamond was the prime suspect. Cotton says that he protected Diamond this time, but he is not sure he can do it anymore. It appears that Diamond has a history of such pranks involving the coal company.

Literary Elements

Plot: Chapters 11–20 introduce the story's two major **external conflicts.** The first is the conflict between George Davis and Lou's friends and family, as evi-

denced by the children's run-in with George at his still and Lou's fight with Billy Davis at school. The second is the conflict between Southern Valley Coal and Gas and Lou's friends and family, revealed in Cotton's description of Diamond's prank on the mine superintendent. Lou's **internal conflict** changes: Her resentment of her mother has died down, but her fear of having her hopes dashed has taken its place.

Theme: The theme of **hope and despair** is deepened in these chapters. Although Lou is outwardly skeptical and resentful of Oz's and Cotton's attempts to reach Amanda, she eventually lets hope temper her despair, making a wish of her own at the wishing well and teaching Oz how to brush Amanda's hair.

Symbol

- The **wishing well** becomes the ruling symbol of the novel in these chapters. It symbolizes the hope that Oz and Lou have for their mother's recovery. Because the wishing well requires a sacrifice of a precious item from those who wish to call on it, the well also stands for the sacrifices that people must make in order to get what is really important to them.

- Diamond's lump of **coal** is an overt symbol for Diamond himself. Rough and unrefined on the outside, within it is believed to lie something of great value. That thing is, appropriately enough, a diamond.

- The **land** becomes an important symbol for life itself in this section of the book. The rugged landscape demands hard work and patience, yet still refuses to offer up its rewards sometimes. For years at a time, the rains will be insufficient or ill timed, and the harvest will be meager. At other times, the season goes perfectly, and the farmers have abundance. Like life itself, the land rewards and punishes seemingly at random.

Chapters 21–30

Plot Synopsis

Billy Davis and Lou have another fight at school, and Ms. McCoy sends for George Davis and Louisa. George hits his son and threatens to take him out of school. Louisa confronts George, and he slurs her American Indian heritage. Later, Louisa talks to Lou about Billy Davis, pointing out how George Davis neglects and abuses his children, in contrast to Lou's father, Jack. Late one night, the children sneak out for another outing with Diamond and Jeb. Jeb takes off after a bear, and the two animals run into George Davis's still, smashing it. In the ensuing chaos, Davis fires a gun at the children, grabs Oz, and hits Lou. Diamond beats Davis with a wooden post, and the children escape. Louisa scolds the children when they get home, especially Lou, whom she holds responsible for Oz's well-being. When Davis shows up the next day demanding payment for the broken still, Louisa refuses, but Diamond pays him off with an antique silver dollar. Davis seems satisfied, and promises to stay off the farm. Two nights later, Davis accompanies some men into a coal mine on Louisa's property.

Louisa tells Lou that Diamond's mother died in childbirth and his father died in an avalanche caused by mine blasting. The mining company refused to pay the boy any compensation, leading to his undying animosity and numerous pranks.

On the Fourth of July, Cotton drives the whole crew to Dickens to see the parade, leaving only Louisa and Amanda behind. Southern Valley Coal and Gas has a large hand in the celebration, and receives effusive praise from the mayor.

Later, Louisa tells Lou that Jack was abandoned by his mother when he was seven and that his father died when he was ten. Billy Davis shows up at the farm late one night, asking Louisa to assist his mother in childbirth. Lou insists on accompanying her. The Davis house is small, filthy, and full of neglected children.

Lou tries to talk to the children, but they are so afraid of her that she finally goes outside, where she talks to Billy for a while. George is in the barn, helping a mare birth a foal. The foal dies, and George approaches Lou, demanding that she and Louisa leave. When it becomes clear that they won't, he tells them to let the baby die if it's a girl. The baby is a boy, and Mrs. Davis names him Lou. As Lou and Louisa leave, Lou notices that the farm itself is large and prosperous looking.

Eugene, Oz, Lou, and Diamond come across a river baptism one day. Eugene and Diamond elect to be baptized, and Diamond collects some of the water in a jar and offers it to Oz to use on Amanda. Oz, oddly, refuses. That night, Lou reads to Oz one of Amanda's old letters to Louisa. Eugene goes into the coal mine on Louisa's property with a stick of dynamite in order to blast out some coal for the winter. While the children wait outside, Jeb chases a squirrel into the mine, and Diamond runs after him. Jeb runs out in time, but Diamond is caught in the blast and killed.

The harvest is a good one, and the family has enough excess to share with George Davis's family and sell at a lumber camp.

Literary Elements

Plot: The **rising action** of this section focuses on the intensifying **external conflict** between George Davis and Lou's family and friends. The conflict with Southern Valley Coal and Gas is given greater depth when Lou discovers that the company was responsible for the death of Diamond's father, yet refused to accept responsibility. A crucial, but seemingly unrelated, plot event is the death of Diamond in a coal mine on Louisa's property.

Themes

Hope and despair: The theme of hope and despair is complicated when Oz refuses Diamond's offer of baptismal water as a cure for Amanda. It could indicate that Oz's faith in his mother's recovery is waning.

Children without parents: In chapters 21–30, the theme of children without parents is continued when Lou learns that both of Diamond's parents are dead, and that her father's mother left him and his father died when Jack was a child. The theme is extended to George Davis's children, who live under such extreme neglect as to be effectively parentless.

Setting: One element of the setting becomes a focal point of the story in chapters 21–30. The coal mine on Louisa's property is being investigated by George Davis and other men; it is also where Diamond dies.

Characterization: In chapters 21–30, characterization begins to focus more on deeds than on appearances, especially in the character of George Davis. His villainous nature is revealed through many of his deeds: He hits his son, keeps an illegal still, fires his shotgun at the children, breaks his promise to stay off Louisa's property, pays more attention to the birth of a foal than to the birth of his own child, and starves his family despite his success as a farmer. Nobler characters also reveal their character through their deeds: Louisa assists Mrs. Davis in childbirth and gives the Davises a share of her harvest; Lou attempts to befriend Billy Davis despite his animosity toward her; Diamond risks and loses his life to save Jeb.

Chapters 31–Epilogue

Plot Synopsis

Lou begins reading magazines and newspapers to her mother. One night, she goes to Diamond's tree house to gather up his belongings. She gives all of them to Oz, except for the lump of coal and a heart-shaped piece of wood with an *L* carved on one side and a *D* on the other. The Cardinals adopt Jeb. The family begins preparing for winter, and the children return to school but do not see Billy Davis there. Lou and Oz, who have the same birthday, celebrate turning thirteen and eight, respectively. They receive handmade presents for the most part, but from Cotton, Lou receives a volume of Walt Whitman's poetry and Oz receives two baseball gloves.

Lou and Oz discover men wearing hardhats and masks in the mine, standing around a pipe sticking into the mine floor. The children are seen and run home to tell Louisa and Cotton what they witnessed. Cotton seems sure that the men have discovered natural gas in the mine. The next day, two men from Southern Valley Coal and Gas show up: Judd Wheeler, the company's chief geologist, and Hugh Miller, the company's vice president. They offer Louisa

$100,000 for her property. She refuses to sell, and the men leave angry. At a church picnic on a following Sunday, a group of angry farmers corners Cotton, claiming that Southern Valley will not buy their land unless Louisa sells hers. Cotton tells them that the decision is Louisa's and he cannot change her mind. George Davis confronts Lou and Oz on the same issue, threatens them, and even raises his hand to hit Lou, but is stopped by Cotton.

One night, Lou finds an envelope in the desk in her room. It is a story her father wrote when he was fifteen, which closely mirrors his father's experience of having a wife who could not take the hard life in the mountains. Lou decides that mountain life is the life for her, however. The barn catches fire one snowy night, killing much of the livestock and destroying most of the tools. Watching the fire, Louisa suffers a stroke and is rushed to the hospital in Dickens, where she remains unconscious. Her doctor, Travis Barnes, is unsure whether she'll recover. Lou, having been robbed of her father, her mother, Diamond, and now Louisa, feels abandoned. Eugene and the children attempt to rebuild the barn using salvaged materials, but they lack the resources to complete the job. A group of farmers, among them those who confronted Cotton about Louisa's refusal to sell, shows up with wagonloads of building materials and builds a new barn under Eugene's direction.

The coal industry is failing, and the lumber industry has moved on, causing economic difficulties in the area. When Cotton and the children visit Louisa in the hospital, angry men confront them and throw rocks at the car. Southern Valley pressures the county tax office to demand payment on Louisa's back taxes. To pay off the debt, Cotton sells all of his books, except for his Jack Cardinal collection, which he gives to Lou. Hugh Miller ups the offer to $500,000, but Cotton continues to refuse on Louisa's behalf. In response, Miller pushes to have Louisa declared mentally unfit to execute her property. Cotton acts as her attorney in the case. He is up against Thurston Goode, an important and well-known lawyer from the state capital. George Davis is on the jury. During court recess, Miller offers to drop the suit if Oz and Lou will simply accept the $500,000. They refuse. That night, they take Amanda's old letters to the wishing well and wish for Louisa's recovery. The next day in court, Cotton is willing to concede that Louisa is mentally unfit if the court will allow him to examine whether Southern Valley is morally fit to run her land. The judge agrees. In questioning Lou, Eugene, and Dr. Barnes, he reveals that the explosion that killed Diamond was too great to have been caused by a single stick of dynamite and was consistent with a natural gas explosion. Under Cotton's questioning, Judd Wheeler reveals that Southern Valley knew the mine was full of gas, yet took no measures to protect the public. Wheeler testifies that, in fact, Miller had told him to say nothing about the gas in order to keep secret Southern Valley's activities on Louisa's property. While the jury deliberates, Lou and Oz return home. Despite Cotton's efforts, the jury finds in favor of Southern Valley. Cotton is told that Louisa has died and announces the news to the court, which must now appoint a guardian for the children. At that moment, Lou and Oz walk in with Amanda between them, and Cotton presents Amanda as the rightful parent and guardian of the children. Amanda and the children retain control of the land. Eventually, Amanda and Cotton marry, and Oz grows up to pitch for the New York Yankees, winning a World Series. Eugene eventually marries and acquires his own farm. Lou leaves the farm for a while, but after marriage, returns to raise her family there and becomes a famous author.

Literary Elements

Plot: In chapters 31–epilogue, the two main **external conflicts** in the story converge as Southern Valley Coal and Gas attempts to take over Louisa's land and George Davis tries to pressure her into selling it to them. After Louisa's stroke, Davis is even on the jury in the trial that will determine whether Louisa is fit to execute her own estate. **Suspense** builds as Cotton loses Louisa's case and then discovers that she has died, leaving unresolved the guardianship of the children. The novel reaches its **climax** as Lou and Oz walk into the courtroom with their recently revived mother between them. The epilogue provides a **denouement,** tying up loose ends and giving a glimpse into the main characters' futures. The issue of where and with whom the children will live is **resolved** by their living on the farm with their mother.

Themes

Hope and despair: Lou appears to be embracing hope by beginning to read magazines to her mother. She almost gives in to despair when Louisa suffers a stroke, but hope wins out when she and Oz make a new wish at the wishing well, hoping for Louisa's recovery. Although Louisa dies, the children's hopes are rewarded when their mother recovers.

Children without parents: Lou and Oz's plight as orphans is deepened when Louisa, their substitute parental figure, suffers a stroke and enters a coma. Their plight is rectified when Amanda recovers.

Plot Synopsis and Literary Elements *(cont.)*

Wish You Well

Symbol

- The **wishing well** serves once again as a symbol of hope as the children leave a new offering, their mother's letters to Louisa, wishing for Louisa's recovery.
- Louisa's **land**—the farm and the mountain on which it sits—has become a symbol of family. The fate of the property becomes the fate of the Cardinal family. Cotton expressly says, "You know she'd never sell her land, because that ground is as much a part of her family as her great-grandchildren. . . . You can't let Southern Valley steal the woman's family."

Figurative Language:

- When Hugh Miller first appears, he is **metaphorically** described as having "snake eyes."

- The narrator **personifies** the mountains when describing the weather on the last day of the trial: " . . . the mountains had grown weary of the rain and had finally broken up the clouds and sent them on their way."

Foreshadowing: The discovery that Southern Valley Coal and Gas has been searching for gas on Louisa's property resolves Diamond's earlier reference to men on local farmers' land.

Irony: Although the children change their wish for Amanda's recovery to a wish for Louisa's recovery, Louisa dies and Amanda recovers.

Reader's Log: Model

Reading actively In your reader's log you record your ideas, questions, comments, interpretations, guesses, predictions, reflections, challenges—any responses you have to the books you are reading.

Keep your reader's log with you while you are reading. You can stop at any time to write. You may want to pause several times during your reading time to capture your thoughts while they are fresh in your mind, or you may want to read without interruption and write when you come to a stopping point such as the end of a chapter or the end of the book.

Each entry you make in your reader's log should include the date, the title of the book you are reading, and the pages you have read since your last entry (pages _____ to _____).

Example

Sept. 21

Fahrenheit 451
pages 3 to 68

This book reminds me a lot of another book we read in class last year, <u>1984</u> by George Orwell. They're both books about the future—<u>1984</u> was written in the 1940s so it was the future then—a bad future where the government is very repressive and you can be arrested for what you think, say, or read. They're also both about a man and a woman who try to go against the system together. <u>Fahrenheit 451</u> is supposed to be about book censorship, but I don't think it's just about that—I think it's also about people losing their brain power by watching TV all the time and not thinking for themselves. <u>1984</u> did not have a very happy ending, and I have a feeling this book isn't going to either.

Exchanging ideas Exchange reader's logs with a classmate and respond in writing to each other's most recent entries. (Your entries can be about the same book or different ones.) You might ask a question, make a comment, give your own opinion, recommend another book— in other words, discuss anything that's relevant to what you are reading.

Or: Ask your teacher, a family member, or a friend to read your most recent entries and write a reply to you in your reader's log.

Or: With your teacher's guidance, find an online pen pal in another town, state, or country and have a continuing book dialogue by e-mail.

Reader's Log: Starters

When I started reading this book, I thought . . .

I changed my mind about . . . because . . .

My favorite part of the book was . . .

My favorite character was . . . because . . .

I was surprised when . . .

I predict that . . .

I liked the way the writer . . .

I didn't like . . . because . . .

This book reminded me of . . .

I would (wouldn't) recommend this book to a friend because . . .

This book made me feel . . .

This book made me think . . .

This book made me realize . . .

While I was reading I pictured . . . (Draw or write your response.)

The most important thing about this book is . . .

If I were (name of character), I would (wouldn't) have . . .

What happened in this book was very realistic (unrealistic) because . . .

My least favorite character was . . . because . . .

I admire (name of character) for . . .

One thing I've noticed about the author's style is . . .

If I could be any character in this book, I would be . . . because . . .

I agree (disagree) with the writer about . . .

I think the title is a good (strange/misleading) choice because . . .

A better title for this book would be . . . because . . .

In my opinion, the most important word (sentence/paragraph) in this book is . . . because . . .

(Name of character) reminds me of myself because . . .

(Name of character) reminds me of somebody I know because . . .

If I could talk to (name of character), I would say . . .

When I finished this book, I still wondered . . .

This book was similar to (different from) other books I've read because it . . .

This book was similar to (different from) other books by this writer because it . . .

I think the main thing the writer was trying to say was . . .

This book was better (worse) than the movie version because . . .

(Event in book) reminded me of (something that happened to me) when . . .

Double-Entry Journal: Models

Responding to the text Draw a line down the middle of a page in your reader's log. On the left side, copy a meaningful passage from the book you're reading— perhaps a bit of dialogue, a description, or a character's thought. (Be sure to note the number of the page you copied it from—you or somebody else may want to find it later.) On the right side, write your response to the quotation. Why did you choose it? Did it puzzle you? confuse you? strike a chord? What does it mean to you?

Example

Quotation	Response
"It is a truth universally acknowledged, that a single man in possession of a good fortune must be in want of a wife." (page 1)	This is the first sentence of the book. When I first read it I thought the writer was serious— it seemed like something people might have believed when it was written. Soon I realized she was making fun of that attitude. I saw the movie Pride and Prejudice, but it didn't have a lot of funny parts, so I didn't expect the book to be funny at all. It is though, but not in an obvious way.

Creating a dialogue journal Draw a line down the middle of a page in your reader's log. On the left side, comment on the book you're reading—the plot so far, your opinion of the characters, or specifics about the style in which the book is written. On the right side of the page, your teacher or a classmate will provide a response to your comments. Together you create an ongoing dialogue about the novel as you are reading it.

Example

Your Comment	Response
The Bennet girls really seem incredibly silly. They seem to care only about getting married to someone rich or going to balls. That is all their parents discuss, too. The one who isn't like that, Mary, isn't realistic either, though. And why doesn't anyone work?!	I wasn't really bothered by their discussion of marriage and balls. I expected it because I saw the movie Emma, and it was like this, too. What I don't understand is why the parents call each other "Mr." and "Mrs."—everything is so formal. I don't think women of that class were supposed to work back then. And people never really work on TV shows or in the movies or in other books, do they?

Name _____ Date _____

Group Discussion Log

Group members

_____

_____

_____

_____

_____

Book discussed

Title: _____

Author: _____

Pages _____ to _____

Three interesting things said by members of the group

_____

_____

_____

_____

_____

_____

_____

What we did well today as a group

_____

_____

_____

What we could improve

_____

_____

_____

_____

Our next discussion will be on _____. We will discuss pages _____ to _____.

Glossary and Vocabulary

- **Vocabulary Words** are preceded by an asterisk (*) and appear in the Vocabulary Worksheets.
- Words are listed in their order of appearance.
- The definition and the part of speech are based on the way the word is used in the chapter. For other uses of the word, check a dictionary.

Chapters 1–10

rangy *adj.:* slender and long-limbed

lanky *adj.:* awkwardly tall and slender

alchemy *n.:* a seemingly magical power to change a thing into something better; in the Middle Ages (c. 476–1450 A.D.), practitioners of alchemy believed there were ways to turn common metals into gold

***volatile** *adj.:* unpredictable; variable

***rejuvenated** *v.:* made to feel or seem young again; made new or fresh

***conciliatory** *adj.:* tending to make friendly or soothe the anger of

crypt *n.:* an underground chamber that serves as a place for burial

***piety** *n.:* devotion or strict attention to religious practices

***sonorous** *adj.:* rich and full of sound; deep

minarets *n.:* tall, slender towers usually attached to a Muslim place of worship; it is from these towers that the people are called to prayer

***pinnacle** *n.:* the highest point

***tenaciously** *adj.:* in a stubborn manner

***enigmatic** *adj.:* mysterious; baffling

ecclesiastical *adj.:* having to do with the church

***eclectic** *adj.:* made of material from many different sources or systems

***privy** *adj.:* privately informed; let in on

topographical *adj.:* showing the surface features of an area, as on a map or chart

***unfathomable** *adj.:* that cannot be understood; deeply mysterious

incantations *n.:* supposedly magical words chanted to perform an act of magic

***incriminating** *adj.:* tending to make appear guilty, as of a crime or misdeed

catatonic *adj.:* marked by a loss of consciousness and feeling

***pedantic** *adj.:* overly academic; in a way that puts emphasis on minor points or ideas in order to show off one's knowledge

***temperate** *adj.:* neither hot nor cold; moderate

lean-to *n.:* a shed with a sloped roof that is supported by the outer wall of another building

pediment *n.:* a low-pitched, triangular roof on the front of a building

portico *n.:* a covered porch or walkway supported by columns

Ionic *adj.:* of a classical type of Greek or Roman architecture known for its ornamental scrolls on the tops of columns

***finite** *adj.:* having definite, measurable borders; limited

macadam *n.:* pavement made with small broken stones mixed with tar or asphalt

brogans *n.:* heavy, high-topped work boots

gingham *n.:* cotton cloth usually woven in a checked or plaid pattern

coal tipple *n.:* the place where coal is emptied by tipping the mine car

***amicable** *adj.:* friendly; peaceful

***ostensibly** *adv.:* seemingly; apparently

***annulling** *v.:* putting an end to; canceling

***chastened** *adj.:* punished in such a way as to correct a fault; scolded

blasphemed *v.:* spoke in a disrespectful way about God or sacred things

doubletreed *v.:* harnessed side by side to a crossbar to which a plow or wagon is attached

spartan *adj.:* plain and lacking luxury

*effusive *adj.:* emotionally unrestrained; gushy

ferrotypes *n.:* old-fashioned photographs taken directly on a thin plate of coated metal

gamut *n.:* the entire range

ticking *n.:* heavy cloth used to cover mattresses or pillows

drugget *n.:* a coarse rug

*pungent *adj:* sharp of smell or taste

Chapters 11–20

*taut *adj.:* tightly stretched

*feigned *v.:* pretended

larynxes *n.:* the structures of muscle and cartilage that contain the human vocal cords

moniker *n.:* name or nickname

*dubious *adj.:* questionable; arousing suspicion or question

chicory *n.:* a root that is roasted and used as a substitute for coffee

surveyors *n.:* people who determine the boundaries of tracts of land by measuring lines and angles with specialized instruments

trumped *v.:* outdid; surpassed

*scintillating *adj.:* witty; intellectually brilliant

*audacity *n.:* bold courage; daring

tincture *n.:* a solution of a medicinal substance

Longfellow: Henry Wadsworth Longfellow, U.S. poet (1807–82)

*irascible *adj.:* irritable; quick-tempered; cranky

gossamer *adj.:* anything thin and filmy as a cobweb

water moccasin *n.:* a large, poisonous snake found in the southeastern United States

puncheon *n.:* a broad piece of rough-cut lumber with one side hewed flat

caliper *n.:* an instrument, similar to tongs, used to measure the diameter of something

connoisseur *n.:* one who has expert knowledge or taste in a particular area

*corpulent *adj.:* fat

*vigilant *adj.:* alert to signs of trouble; watchful

*meticulously *adv.:* extremely carefully; with great attention to detail

Chapters 21–30

scythes *n.:* a long-handled cutting tool with a long, curved blade

phosphorus *n.:* a chemical element that gives off light after being exposed to light

vaudeville *n.:* a stage show made up of songs, dances, comedy skits, and other performances

gramophone *n.:* an old-fashioned device that plays sounds that have been mechanically etched on a circular disk

*gingerly *adv.:* cautiously; in a careful way

*ingenuity *n.:* cleverness; resourcefulness

knoll *n.:* a mound or small hill

*exuberant *adj.:* full of life; high-spirited

*unbridled *adj.:* free from any restraint; uncontrolled

titanic *adj.:* of great size or strength

Sacraments *n.:* in the Catholic Church, the rites of baptism, confirmation, the Eucharist (Communion), penance, holy orders, matrimony, and Anointing of the Sick

Creed *n.:* the Apostles' Creed, a statement of belief in the basic Christian doctrines

Rosary *n.:* a string of beads used in praying

Mortal Sins *n.:* sins which are considered such serious offenses that they would prevent one from entering Heaven unless confessed before death

Venial Sins *n.:* those sins which are not of sufficient seriousness to prevent one from entering Heaven

First Confession *n.:* the full statement of religious beliefs and confession of one's sins made before the First Communion may be taken

First Communion *n.:* the rite in which one who has made his or her First Confession participates in the Eucharist

Confirmation *n.:* ceremony in which one is admitted to full membership in the Catholic Church

Sacrament of Extreme Unction *n.:* also known as the Anointing of the Sick; a rite in which a priest prays for a person who is dying or is gravely ill

*considered *adj.:* well thought out

maelstrom *n.:* a violent state of affairs

shocks *n.:* bundles of grain stacked together on end to dry

Chapters 31–Epilogue

eulogy *n.:* a speech praising a person who has recently died

*diligently *adv.:* busily; in a careful, steady, hard-working manner

*atone *v.:* to apologize; to make up for a bad action

circuit minister *n.:* a minister who travels throughout a certain area to hold services at designated places

*lax *adj.:* morally loose; reckless

crackling bread *n.:* bread cooked with crisped bits of hog fat

*prowess *n.:* superior skill; great talent

darning *v.:* mending by sewing stitches across a hole or tear

*tainting *v.:* making less than pure; corrupting

exact *v.:* to force or demand

hearth *n.:* the floor of a fireplace

*squalor *n.:* extreme misery; filth

dole *n.:* money or food, usually given out by the government, to those who are in need

studs *n.:* upright timbers or beams in the walls of a building

*slander *n.:* a false statement that harms someone's reputation; misrepresentation

*ominous *adj.:* threatening

hackles *n.:* the hairs that stand up on the back of a dog's neck when it is ready to fight

*luminous *adj.:* glowing

mortise *n.:* a hole or notch cut in a piece of wood to receive a projecting part designed to fit into it

tenon *n.:* the projecting part cut at the end of a piece of wood to join it to another by fitting into a mortise

forge *n.:* a place where metal is heated and hammered into shape

shoeing anvil *n.:* a heavy iron block on which horseshoes are hammered into shape

block and tackle *n.:* an arrangement of pulleys, ropes, and weights to aid in raising heavy objects

coke *n.:* coal from which most gases have been removed by heating

*pallor *n.:* paleness; lack of color

throttled *v.:* strangled; choked

bivouac *n.:* a temporary camp, especially one out in the open

*sublime *adj.:* noble; awe-inspiring

served *v.:* to deliver a formal legal document

*portly *adj.:* large or heavy, especially in a dignified way

*lucrative *adj.:* well paying; profitable

*circumvent *v.:* to go around; to thwart

recuse *v.:* to withdraw as a judge because of a personal interest or conflict in a case

Zeus: the chief deity of Greek mythology

semantical *adj.:* having to do with the meaning of language

*gamely *adv.:* in a determined, courageous manner

voir dired *v.:* examined potential witnesses or jurors in a legal case to determine their fitness to testify or serve

*propensity *n.:* natural disposition; tendency

sidebar *n.:* a discussion among the judge and attorneys in a legal matter carried on outside the hearing of the jury

ex parte: *(Latin)* in the interest of only one side

Wish You Well

broadsides *n.:* forceful verbal attacks

*ponderous *adj.:* awkwardly heavy; bulky

*benignly *adv.:* in a kindly, good-natured manner

*indomitable *adj.:* that cannot be discouraged or conquered

*ironic *adj.:* meaning the opposite of what is said or written

*conducive *adj.:* that contributes or leads to

of his own accord: without being asked; by his own ability

cipher *v.:* to solve arithmetic problems

*errant *adj.:* stray; wandering

*exemplary *adj.:* worthy of imitation; model

First Thoughts

1. What, in your opinion, is the greatest adjustment that Lou and Oz will have to make?

2. What kind of person do you think Louisa (Lou and Oz's great-grandmother) is? Why?

Shaping Interpretations

3. Lou's parents are arguing right before the car accident. How does this circumstance affect Lou's attitude toward Amanda?

4. Why do you think Lou gets Oz's necklace back for him after the nurse takes it away?

5. Contrast Louisa's treatment of the nurse with her treatment of Oz, Lou, and Amanda. What accounts for this difference?

6. Why is it significant that in Lou's room is a desk with her father's initials carved into it?

READING CHECK

a. Why do Lou and Oz go with their mother to live with their great-grandmother?

b. What is odd about Amanda's condition?

c. How does Oz attempt to heal his mother?

d. What modern amenities does the Cardinals' new home lack?

e. What information that Diamond provides at dinner is of interest to Louisa?

f. Why does Eugene stay with Louisa?

Connecting with the Text

7. Lou has an experience that puts her in a new place, emotionally and psychologically. She takes a parallel physical journey to a new place far from everything she has known. In other books, movies, or TV shows you know, what physical journeys have other characters taken that mirror their emotional or psychological changes?

Extending the Text

8. When Lou and Oz first meet Diamond, he tells them that Eugene's name is Hell No, and that he received that name when his father abandoned him. Later, the children learn Eugene's real name and are told that he was not abandoned at all. Why do you think people start rumors like this one and then continue to spread them even after the truth is made known?

Challenging the Text

9. Baldacci uses nonstandard spelling, usage, and punctuation to represent the dialect of some of his characters. Does this representation of dialect speech improve or impede your understanding and enjoyment of the text? Explain.

Reading Strategies: Chapters 1–10

Wish You Well

Understanding Characterization

By paying attention to how Lou reacts to events and circumstances around her, we learn about Lou's character.

In the second ring of the circle, summarize Lou's reaction to each event or circumstance. In the outer ring, explain what this reaction tells us about Lou's character.

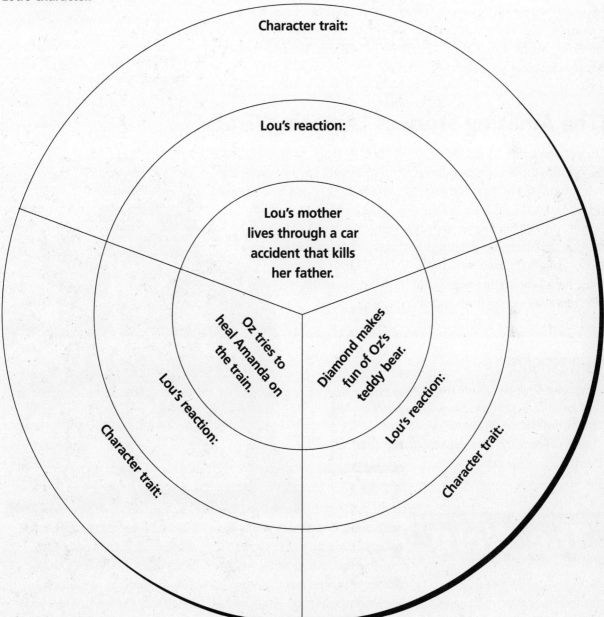

Character trait:

Lou's reaction:

Lou's mother lives through a car accident that kills her father.

Oz tries to heal Amanda on the train.

Diamond makes fun of Oz's teddy bear.

Lou's reaction:

Lou's reaction:

Character trait:

Character trait:

FOLLOW-UP: Review the character traits you have listed in the outer ring. Based on what you know about Lou's new living situation, write a paragraph on a separate sheet of paper predicting where these character traits will lead Lou.

Novel Notes

Chapters 1–10, *Wish You Well*

The Appalachians: Longer Than a Walk to School!

Some intrepid walkers have tried to cover the 1,600 miles of the Appalachian mountain chain, which runs southward from the Gaspé Peninsula in Quebec, Canada, to the Gulf coastal plain of Alabama. The Appalachians are rocky remainders of a great mountain mass that was formed by folds in the earth's crust. Some famous parts of the range include the Green Mountains of Vermont and the Blue Ridge Mountains of Pennsylvania and Virginia.

FOR YOUR READER'S LOG

If you were interviewed for an oral history, what important stories about your life would you tell?

The Amazing Story of "Amazing Grace"

The popular hymn "Amazing Grace" has traveled the world many times over. Composed by John Newton (1725–1807), a British slave-ship captain, priest, hymn writer and abolitionist, the hymn was published in 1779. "Amazing Grace" is widely loved for its comforting message of forgiveness as well as its memorable tune. Its many versions include a successful bagpipe recording made in 1972 and a version sung by Mahalia Jackson in 1947. It was used as a civil rights ballad by Dr. Martin Luther King, Jr., in the 1960s.

Mahalia Jackson

INVESTIGATE

Lou and Oz travel to the wilderness of Virginia to start their new lives. Do they leave behind any traces of "wilderness" in New York City? Research the five boroughs of the city.

The Word PLACE

Yankee

Generally used as a nickname for a native of New England or the northern United States, the origins of the word *Yankee* are numerous. One theory is that the word derives from *Yengee,* a North American Indian word for the English, and that this word evolved into Yankee. Another theory is that Yankee comes from Jan Kees, a nickname the English had for the Dutch in the New World. In any event, British soldiers in the French and Indian War prior to 1758 referred to New Englanders as Yankees. Eventually the word, when used overseas, came to refer to Americans in general.

Choices: Chapters 1–10

Building Your Portfolio

CREATIVE WRITING

In the Driver's Seat

On the trip from the train station to the farm, Eugene drives the car but says very little, even though some interesting things happen. Re-read the scene in which Eugene picks up the children and drives them home. As you read, look for clues to Eugene's reactions to sights and events. Then, rewrite the scene from Eugene's point of view.

PERFORMANCE

Sibling Quibbling

Like many siblings, Lou has conflicting feelings about her little brother, Oz. With a small group of students, select and act out two short scenes from the book: one in which Lou is critical of Oz, and one in which she is supportive of him. Discuss with the class why Lou might feel differently about Oz from one scene to the next. What external or internal circumstances influence her behavior?

ART

First Impressions

When Lou and Oz first arrive at their new home, the property is described in detail. Using the text as a reference, create a drawing or painting of the farm as Lou and Oz first see it. Accompany your artwork with a caption—perhaps a quotation from the novel that sums up your take on the farm—and display it in the classroom.

Consider This . . .

"Some say believing a person get better is half the battle. I'm one who subscribes to that notion."

Louisa says these words to comfort Oz. Do you think she actually believes what she says, or is she just helping Oz get through a difficult time?

Writing Follow-up: Persuasion

Do you agree with Louisa's statement? Take a position defending or disagreeing with her claim that believing a person will get better assists that person's healing process. Give at least two reasons for your position, and support each reason with examples or facts.

Novel Notes

Create an activity based on **Novel Notes, Issue 1.** Here are two suggestions.

- Research the wildlife of the Appalachians.
- Listen to different recordings of "Amazing Grace" and say which one you like best and why.

First Thoughts

1. Lou picks a fight with Billy Davis. Do you think her actions are justified? Why or why not?

Shaping Interpretations

2. What does the children's run-in with George Davis reveal about his **character**?

3. Why will Lou not talk to or read to her mother?

4. What does the wishing well **symbolize** for Lou and Oz?

5. In the café in Dickens, what kind of discrimination do the children, particularly Diamond, experience?

6. Why does Cotton accept payment in the form of goods such as food, blankets, and lanterns?

READING CHECK

a. What are Lou, Oz, and Diamond doing outside at night when they unexpectedly run across George Davis?

b. Why is Davis guarding the area with a shotgun?

c. According to Diamond, how does the wishing well work?

d. After Lou shows disdain for Oz's desire to tell Amanda about the birth of a calf, what does Louisa give Lou?

e. What is Lou's first day at school like?

f. What do Lou and Oz wish for at the wishing well?

7. How does Diamond react to Cotton's news that horse manure was found in the mine superintendent's car? Why does he react this way?

Connecting with the Text

8. When Lou, Oz, and Diamond are in Dickens, Diamond is suddenly out of his element. On the mountain, he is more knowledgeable and experienced than his friends, but in Dickens, they must explain his experiences and tell him how to behave. Describe a time when you were out of your element. How did you deal with the situation?

Extending the Text

9. As Lou and Oz go searching for wayward cows, the narrator comments, "Eugene had let the cows and the calf out to graze in the open field, and, as cows, like people, were wont to do, they were wandering the countryside looking for better prospects." Do you think the comparison is apt? In other words, are people usually willing to leave what they know in hopes of finding something better? Explain your answer and provide examples.

Challenging the Text

10. Do you think it is believable that Lou's father happens to be Cotton's favorite author? Explain your answer.

Reading Strategies: Chapters 11–20

Wish You Well

Comparing and Contrasting

Lou and Oz, as brother and sister, share much in common but also have many differences.

Fill in the ovals to compare and contrast Lou and Oz.

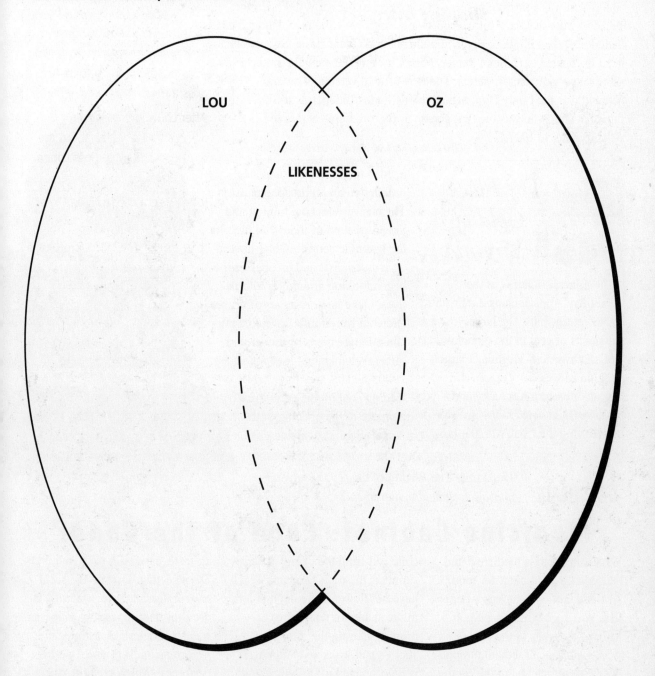

FOLLOW-UP: Which character do you like more, Lou or Oz? Why? Write your answer in a paragraph on a separate sheet of paper. Include details about both characters from the diagram.

Novel Notes

Chapters 11–20, *Wish You Well*

Onto the Dance Floor: Music of the Day

Dancing the jitterbug at a drugstore after school? As bizarre as that might sound, that was a favorite pastime of teenagers in the early 1940s. In the decade before that, jazz-influenced swing bands were the rage. Famous bands included Duke Ellington, Benny Goodman, and Count Basie. Swing dancing itself originated in Harlem, in New York City, cultural capital—in the 1920s, as it is now—of black America. The first official version of swing dancing was the Lindy Hop, named after Charles Lindbergh, the famed aviator who was the first person to fly (or "hop") across the Atlantic solo, in 1927.

READER'S LOG

Consider Oz and Cotton's hope for Amanda's recovery. Have you ever been in a similar situation? Why was it worth the wait?

History in a Nutshell: *The Black Gold of Virginia*

The mineral richness of the Southern Appalachians didn't stay a secret for long. The large deposits of coal in the mountains of southwestern Virginia, a large region of western Virginia and parts of eastern Kentucky and Alabama attracted many investors. Following the Civil War, the U.S. needed to fuel its iron and steel production and railroad expansion. The answer was coal mining and the production of industrial fuel. In the late nineteenth century, however, industrialists and prospectors began looking around for alternatives. Once large reserves of timber and coal were found, investors purchased huge tracts of timber and mineral-rich land at low prices. By 1900, the U.S. was the world's leading coal producer, in great part due to the opening of the Appalachian coal fields.

INVESTIGATE *What made* The Wizard of Oz *(1939) such an amazing technical achievement?*

Medicine Cabinet: Food of the Gods?

What stinks but is medicinal and is used as a condiment for food? Asafetida, of course! And what is that, you ask? Why, it's the gum resin of the roots of the *Ferula assa-foetida* plant. Found throughout eastern Asia and in the central U.S., this herb has a large fleshy root and a stem that can range from six to ten feet high. Juice is collected from the plants in early summer; the roots of plants which have not flowered are cut and left in the shade for one to two months. During that time, the sticky resin leaks and hardens. It is then scraped off in lumps and treated before being sold. The milky resin has a strong oniony or garlicky (or both) scent and a bitter taste, earning it the name Devil's Dung. Despite the scent and unpleasant taste, asafetida is used for treating various ailments such as indigestion, asthma and hypertension. It is also used in perfumes, Worcestershire sauce, and as an ingredient in sauces and gravies.

Choices: Chapters 11–20

Building Your Portfolio

CREATIVE WRITING

The Land of Oz

What if Oz were to keep a journal of his thoughts? What would he write about his experiences on the mountain? Write a short series of journal entries, about four or five, that Oz might have written. Choose particular days—for example, the day the children found the wishing well, or the day they went to Dickens—and write an entry for each day. How does Oz feel about each day's events?

MUSIC

Town and Country

The children's visit to Dickens provides a revealing contrast to their life on the mountain. Find recordings of songs or parts of songs that, to you, fit the mood and pace of life on the mountain. Then, find other recordings that fit the mood and pace of life in Dickens. Make a tape of these recordings, and play it for the class. Be prepared to explain your selections.

TABLEAU

What Were You Thinking?

With a small group, choose a scene from chapters 11–20 in which one or more of the protagonists has a confrontation with another character, such as the children's run-in with George Davis, Lou's fight with Billy Davis, or the children's encounter with the café proprietor. Assign each group member a character, and freeze the scene in place. Then, each character should "unfreeze" one at a time and explain what he or she is thinking during the scene. Include gestures and facial expressions to convey characters' personalities. Afterward, be prepared to discuss how it felt to be your character and why you chose the gestures and expressions that helped you express the character's personality.

Consider This. . .

She grabbed Billy by his overall straps and threw him to the dirt, where he lay stunned, probably both at her strength and at her audacity.

What has Billy done to provoke Lou into attacking him? What does this passage reveal about Lou's way of dealing with conflict?

Writing Follow-up: Problem-Solution ⎯▪

What seems to be the source of the problem that Lou and Oz have with Billy Davis? Write a paragraph summarizing the problem and proposing a solution that will satisfy both Billy and the Cardinal children.

Novel Notes

Create an activity based on **Novel Notes, Issue 2.** Here are two suggestions.

- Research the history of coal mining and find out where the richest deposits in North America are.
- Investigate the history of popular music in the 1940s and list the top three performing stars.

First Thoughts

1. Are you surprised by George Davis's treatment of his family? Why or why not?

Shaping Interpretations

2. Why do you think Cotton carries Amanda outside when the children are learning to ride a horse?

3. How do you explain Louisa's willingness to help the Davises despite George Davis's behavior?

4. How does Lou's relationship with Billy Davis change in this part of the book?

5. Why is it significant that Oz refuses the jar of baptismal water that Diamond offers him?

6. What is **ironic** about Diamond's death?

7. An important **theme** in *Wish You Well* is that of children without parents. How is this theme expanded in chapters 21–30?

READING CHECK

a. What prompts Ms. McCoy to call George Davis and Louisa to the school?

b. Why does George Davis show up at the Cardinal farm, demanding payment?

c. What event sparked Diamond's undying animosity toward Southern Valley Coal and Gas?

d. How does Lou finally get to see the Davis home?

e. What striking contrast does Lou notice between George Davis's home and farm?

f. Why does Diamond run into the mine?

g. What do the Cardinals do with the excess from their harvest?

Connecting with the Text

8. The Fourth of July festivities in Dickens are clearly sponsored to some degree by Southern Valley Coal and Gas. Southern Valley has paid for a float devoted to coal mining, and the mayor, flanked by Southern Valley executives, gives a speech praising the mining company. Company sponsorship of events is commonplace today. What are some examples of these events? What is your opinion of this kind of sponsorship?

Extending the Text

9. Southern Valley Coal and Gas refuses to take responsibility for the harm it has caused others. What real-world examples can you think of in which a business or organization attempted to avoid responsibility for harm it had caused?

Challenging the Text

10. George Davis is a thoroughly despicable character who beats his children, starves his family, threatens people, and breaks promises. Is he an effective villain, or would a more ambiguous character be more convincing? Explain your answer.

Reading Strategies: Chapters 21–30

Wish You Well

Summarizing

The Cardinals and their friends have many important experiences in chapters 21–30. Characters change, grow, and leave.

- **Choose four important events that happen in chapters 21–30.**
- **Write the events in chronological order in the ovals.**

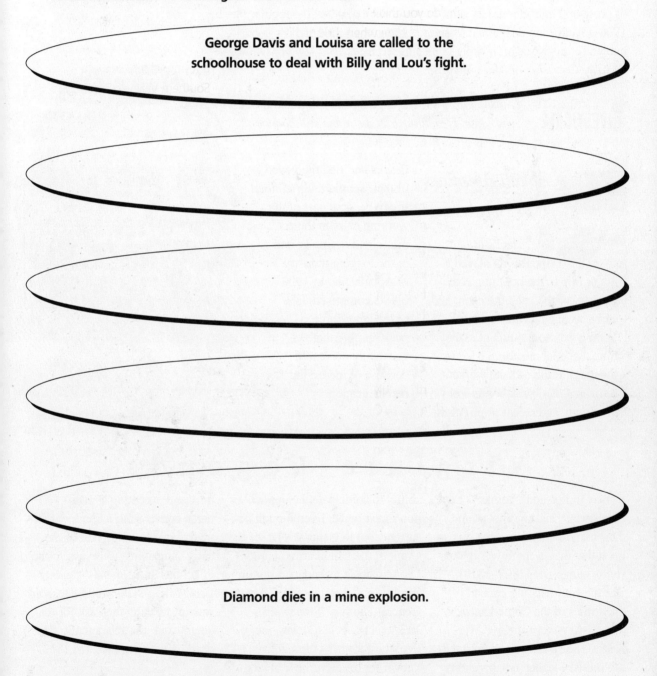

George Davis and Louisa are called to the schoolhouse to deal with Billy and Lou's fight.

Diamond dies in a mine explosion.

FOLLOW-UP: Which of the above events do you think is the most significant? Why? Write your answer in a paragraph on a separate sheet of paper.

Novel Not📖s

Issue 3

Thomas "Stonewall" Jackson

Chapters 21–30, *Wish You Well*

Henry Wadsworth Longfellow: Schoolroom Poet

An author whose work is frequently recited in schools, Henry Wadsworth Longfellow (1807–1882) was a poet, translator, dramatist, orator, and writer of prose and nonfiction. His work became so internationally popular that by 1900 it had been translated into eighteen languages. Longfellow is best known for his lyricism, notably in his masterpieces, *The Song of Hiawatha* and *The Courtship of Miles Standish*.

INVESTIGATE *Louisa helps Mrs. Davis give birth to her child in her own home. Is childbirth in the home still common?*

FOR YOUR READER'S LOG

If you were Louisa, would you have given some of your excess harvest to the Davis family?

 History in a Nutshell:

African Americans in Appalachia

Blacks in Appalachia played a major role in the booming coal industry of the late nineteenth and early twentieth centuries. Coal mining was so prominent at that time that a labor shortage led to the mass hiring of local workers, African American laborers from the South, and recent immigrants.

Blacks had fled the poverty of their southern agricultural life to become part of the working class in the coal mines and railroads, and in the logging industry, of Appalachia. In 1900, blacks comprised 38% of the labor force, a peak number that eventually decreased because of increasing mechanization.

Henry Wadsworth Longfellow

Virginia Legends

Robert E. Lee and Thomas "Stonewall" Jackson's love for their home state of Virginia was so great that they went to war in their state's name. Lee (1807–1870) was the commanding general of the armies of the Confederacy during the American Civil War (1861–1865). He was an outstanding military leader, notably in his ability to aniticipate the opposition's next move. Even though he surrendered to General Ulysses S. Grant of the Union army in 1865, Lee remains a legendary figure in Virginia and throughout the South. General Thomas "Stonewall" Jackson (1824–1863) was one of Lee's best-known commanders, known for his cleverness in planning and executing strategy. His name comes from a comment made by Lee during one of the early campaigns of the war to the effect that Jackson was standing firm, "like a stone wall." Jackson was mistaken in the dark for the enemy and was accidentally shot dead by his own troops in 1863.

Choices: Chapters 21–30

Building Your Portfolio

CREATIVE WRITING

Remembering a Friend

A common way to commemorate a person who has recently died is to give a eulogy—a speech praising the person. Write a eulogy for Diamond that you might deliver to his friends. The eulogy should be at least two paragraphs long and should include details about Diamond from the book.

READING STRATEGIES

Predicting

With a partner, discuss the following aspects of George Davis's character in these chapters:

- his priorities
- his attitude toward the Cardinals
- his activities at night

What might Davis do in the following chapters? Given his personality and behavior in chapters 21–30, what might he have in store for the Cardinal family?

DANCE

Stroll the Floor

With a few of your classmates, choreograph an informal dance like the one in chapter 24. Assign each group member a character, and then assign that character a dance style that suits his or her personality. Choose appropriate music and perform your dance for the class.

Consider This . . .

As they drove the wagon out, they passed corrals filled with enough cattle to qualify as a herd, and hogs and sheep, a yard full of hens, four fine horses, and double that number of mules. The crop fields extended as far as the eye could see, and dangerous barbed wire encircled all of it.

Why is Lou surprised by what she finds at the Davis farm? How does this passage contradict what she already knows about Billy?

Writing Follow-up:
Comparison and Contrast _____ ■

Write two to four paragraphs comparing and contrasting Lou's living situation with Billy's. How do their different situations affect the way they treat others?

Novel Notes

Create an activity based on **Novel Notes, Issue 3.** Here are two suggestions.

- Research famous commanders on the Union side in the Civil War.
- Read *The Song of Hiawatha* in class and discuss it in groups.

Making Meanings: Chapters 31–Epilogue

First Thoughts

1. What troubles you the most about the court case against Louisa?

Shaping Interpretations

2. What are some ways Lou and Oz deal with their grief over Diamond's death?

3. Why are Cotton's old baseball gloves such an apt gift for Oz?

4. Why has Miller been trying to hide Southern Valley's exploration on Louisa's property?

5. How do you explain the locals' reaction to Louisa's refusal to sell?

6. What is Miller's interest in whether Louisa has given Cotton power of attorney?

7. An important **theme** in *Wish You Well* is that of hope and despair. How does Lou and Oz's last visit to the wishing well inform that theme?

8. In what scene does the **climax** of the novel occur? Why might the climax be interpreted as ironic?

READING CHECK

a. What do Lou and Oz discover in the coal mine?

b. Why does Hugh Miller offer Louisa $100,000 for her property?

c. What happens to Louisa while she watches the barn burning?

d. How is the barn rebuilt?

e. How does Cotton pay off Louisa's tax debt?

f. After Cotton refuses Hugh Miller's offer of $500,000, what does Miller do to gain control of Louisa's property?

g. How is the issue of the children's future resolved?

Extending the Text

9. Cotton represents Louisa even though he knows her position is unpopular. Think of another figure, in literature or history, who stood up for a cause that was unpopular or personally dangerous. Who was that figure, what cause did he or she represent, and why did he or she choose to represent it?

Challenging the Text

10. An improbable and abrupt event or character brought into a story to favorably settle a complicated situation is known as a *deus ex machina*. A device of this kind is used at the end of *Wish You Well* to resolve the Cardinal family's difficulties. How convincing do you find this resolution? Would a more realistic ending have been more satisfying? Explain.

Reading Strategies: Chapters 31–Epilogue

Wish You Well

Making Inferences

Often in *Wish You Well*, the narrator or characters do not say everything they mean. It is up to the reader to take what is said in the context in which it is said and infer the total meaning of a statement.

In the right-hand side of the diagram below, write your inference based on each quotation from *Wish You Well*.

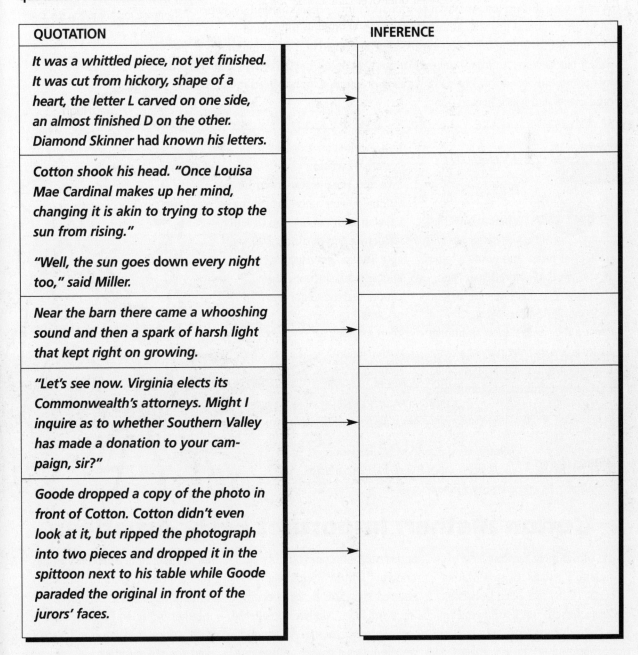

QUOTATION	INFERENCE
It was a whittled piece, not yet finished. It was cut from hickory, shape of a heart, the letter L carved on one side, an almost finished D on the other. Diamond Skinner had known his letters.	
Cotton shook his head. "Once Louisa Mae Cardinal makes up her mind, changing it is akin to trying to stop the sun from rising." *"Well, the sun goes down every night too," said Miller.*	
Near the barn there came a whooshing sound and then a spark of harsh light that kept right on growing.	
"Let's see now. Virginia elects its Commonwealth's attorneys. Might I inquire as to whether Southern Valley has made a donation to your campaign, sir?"	
Goode dropped a copy of the photo in front of Cotton. Cotton didn't even look at it, but ripped the photograph into two pieces and dropped it in the spittoon next to his table while Goode paraded the original in front of the jurors' faces.	

FOLLOW-UP: Why do you think authors often say less than they mean? How effective is Baldacci at this technique? Explain.

Cotton Mather

Chapters 31–Epilogue, *Wish You Well*

Natural Gas: Underground Energy

Natural gas is found deep in the ground and is produced in the same natural process that creates petroleum, or oil: Organic material (for example, algae) is covered with dirt and rock for millions of years. The pressure and lack of oxygen cause this organic material to transform into oil and natural gas. For a long time, natural gas was more of a nuisance than a useful natural resource. But, with the development of safer pipelines, in the last hundred years it has become an important part of many people's lives. Perhaps the most commonly used form of natural gas is propane, which is used in many home ovens and water heaters.

FOR YOUR READER'S LOG

If you had been Judge Atkins, what decision would you have made regarding the future of Louisa Mae Cardinal's property?

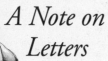

History in a Nutshell:

A Note on Letters

When was the last time you sat down with a sheet of paper and wrote a letter? If you lived a hundred years ago, the answer to that question would probably have been "Yesterday" or "Just a few weeks ago." In human history, letters have played a very important role in keeping people, especially families, in communica-tion. Almost as soon as a system of writing was invented, people started writing letters to each other. In fact, we have an entire collection of letters written in Egypt over 3,700 years ago. Today, letter writing is less widespread, since most people use the telephone or e-mail to keep in touch with friends or family.

INVESTIGATE *What does the term* voir dire *mean in a courtroom? What does the phrase mean in French?*

Cotton Mather: Important Early American

One of the most famous New England Puritans, Cotton Mather (1663–1728) was born in Boston, Massachusetts, and, following in his father's footsteps, later became an important religious minister. At the age of 12, already able to read and write Latin, and already knowing a little Greek, Mather entered Harvard. Before becom-ing a minister, Mather considered a career in medicine. Although he rejected it as a career, throughout his life Mather remained interest-ed in medicine, especially in the prevention of smallpox, a deadly infectious disease. During his life, Mather wrote and published over 400 works, mostly on religious and scientific topics.

Choices: Chapters 31–Epilogue

Wish You Well

Building Your Portfolio

CREATIVE WRITING

Happily Ever After

Wish You Well ends with an epilogue titled "Today" that brings the surviving characters up to the present, but leaves out the details of their lives in between. Now you can fill in some of those details! Write a short short story that takes place in the life of one of the characters—Lou, Oz, Eugene, Amanda, or Cotton—between chapter 40 and the present day. Write about an important event, a funny occurrence, or a typical day, as long as it fits what we know about the character.

DEBATE

Southern Valley v. the Cardinals

With a group of classmates, debate the points in the court case regarding Louisa's competence. One side should take Southern Valley's position, and the other should take the Cardinals' position. Hold the debate and have the class decide the winner.

ART

Mountain Memories

Create a collage to represent the memories Lou might have as an adult looking back at her time on the mountain. Use any materials you like, but be sure to select elements that represent Lou's experiences, companions, and emotions in that time. Display your collage for the class, and be prepared to discuss the choices you've made.

Consider This . . .

"In order to fully protect Miss Cardinal's rights in this matter, we are seeking to have her declared mentally unfit, and to have a guardian appointed so that an orderly disposition of her affairs may be conducted, including this very lucrative offer from Southern Valley."

What do you think are the real motives behind the case brought against Louisa? Why does the Commonwealth's attorney attempt to hide these motives while stating the Commonwealth's position?

Writing Follow-up: Cause-Effect ━━━━━ ■

What circumstances and actions bring about the court case against Louisa? What effects does the case have on her family and on the community? In two to four paragraphs, explain the causes and effects of the court case. Consider both physical circumstances and human motives.

Novel Notes

Create an activity based on **Novel Notes, Issue 4.** Here are two suggestions.

- Learn more about the history of colonial Boston.
- Find out when and where petroleum was first discovered in the United States.

Novel Review

MAJOR CHARACTERS

Use the chart below to keep track of the characters in this book. Each time you come across a new character, write the character's name and the number of the page on which the character first appears. Then, jot down a brief description. Add information about the characters as you read. Put a star next to the name of each main character.

NAME OF CHARACTER	DESCRIPTION

FOLLOW-UP: A *dynamic character* changes in some important way as a result of the story's action. In a paragraph, trace the transformation of one dynamic character from the time the character is introduced through the conclusion of the novel.

Novel Review (cont.)

Wish You Well

SETTING

Time ....

Most important place(s) ....

....

One effect of setting on plot, theme, or character ....

....

....

PLOT

List key events from the novel.

- ....
- ....
- ....

- ....
- ....
- ....

Use your list to identify the plot elements below. Add other events as necessary.

Major conflict / problem ....

....

Turning point / climax ....

....

Resolution / denouement ....

....

MAJOR THEMES

- ....
- ....
- ....

Literary Elements Worksheet 1

Theme

A **theme** is a central, important idea in a work. One of the main themes of *Wish You Well* is Children Without Parents.

Which characters in *Wish You Well* lack parents or the guidance and support that parents provide? Complete the web below with the names of characters who further the theme of Children Without Parents and a brief explanation of how they further that theme.

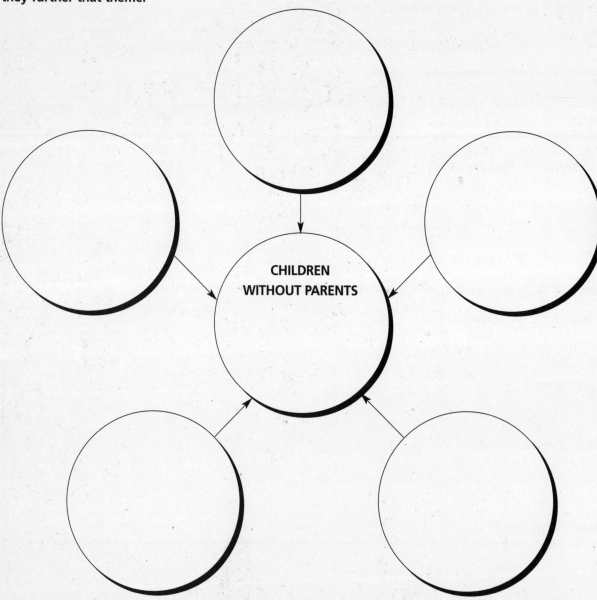

CHILDREN WITHOUT PARENTS

FOLLOW-UP: In one or two paragraphs on a separate sheet of paper, explain why the author might have chosen to make children without parents a recurring theme throughout the novel, rather than restricting it to just the main characters.

Literary Elements Worksheet 2

Wish You Well

Symbol

A symbol is a person, place, thing, or event that stands both for itself and for something beyond itself. In *Wish You Well,* the meanings of two of the most important symbols change as the book progresses.

In the rectangle below each symbol, write the symbol's meaning when it is first encountered in the book. In the second rectangle, write the meaning that the symbol comes to have later in the book.

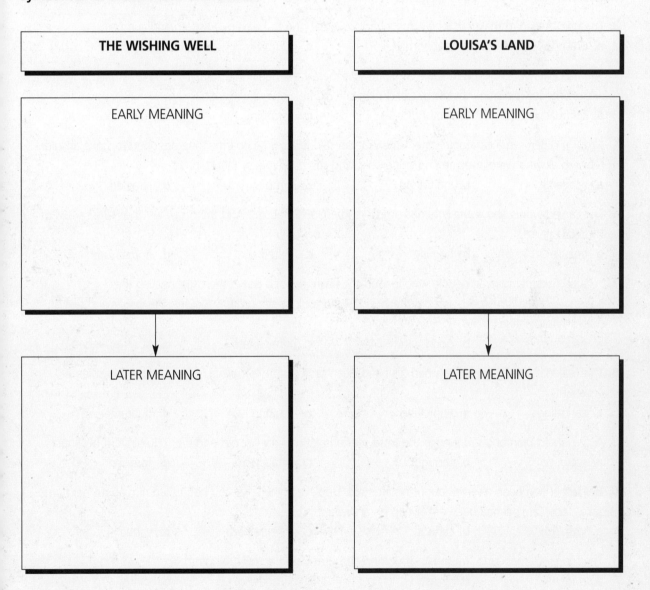

THE WISHING WELL	LOUISA'S LAND
EARLY MEANING	EARLY MEANING
LATER MEANING	LATER MEANING

FOLLOW-UP: Which of the above symbols do you think is the more effective? Why? Write your answer in one or two paragraphs on a separate sheet of paper.

Vocabulary Worksheet 1

Wish You Well

A. Circle the letter of the word or phrase that most nearly defines the italicized word in each excerpt from *Wish You Well*.

1. Amanda took it as good-naturedly as she did most things having to do with her *volatile* daughter.
   a. kindly   **b.** unpredictable   **c.** irresponsible   **d.** talented

2. Amanda glanced at Lou, but even as she tried to think of something *conciliatory* to say, her daughter proved swifter.
   a. soothing   **b.** intelligent   **c.** congratulatory   **d.** insulting

3. The priest stood at the altar, long arms *tenaciously* reaching to heaven's wisdom and comfort…
   a. prayerfully   **b.** stubbornly   **c.** humbly   **d.** stiffly

4. She had listened to the priest say that death was merely the beginning, that in God's *enigmatic* way this was a time for rejoicing, not sorrow, and then she did not listen anymore.
   a. spiritual   **b.** methodical   **c.** disturbing   **d.** mysterious

5. "Your mother is in a catatonic state," the woman said in a cold, *pedantic* tone designed to strike absolute terror in all who were insecure and vulnerable, and she had an easy target in Oz.
   a. academic   **b.** indifferent   **c.** abrupt   **d.** strained

6. The carved words above the columns simply read: "Court House." And then they left the *finite* sprawl of Dickens behind.
   a. peculiar   **b.** homely   **c.** limited   **d.** immeasurable

7. . . . Lou had met colored people who loaded the trash, flagged down the cabs, heaved the bags, . . . cooked the food, and did the laundry, and took, in *amicable* measures, the insults and tips of their white clientele.
   a. necessary   **b.** good-natured   **c.** unfortunate   **d.** absent-minded

8. This sealed it for Oz. He sadly wiped his hand clean on the seat, *annulling* his and Diamond's solemn covenant.
   a. canceling   **b.** approving   **c.** insulting   **d.** guaranteeing

9. A *chastened* Diamond slumped in the front seat and let Jeb idly lick dirt and worm juice from his fingers.
   a. scolded   **b.** thoughtful   **c.** exhausted   **d.** forgiven

10. Her father had been reserved about his life here. However, whenever Lou had asked him about her name-sake, Jack Cardinal had been *effusive* in his answer.
    a. unselfish   **b.** serious   **c.** unrestrained   **d.** vague

11. The room was dark and the smells of damp and burnt wood equally *pungent*.
    a. evident   **b.** sweet   **c.** nauseating   **d.** sharp

12. The man smiled and shook Louisa's hand. "Well, since I'm also one of the very few lawyers round here, that's a *dubious* distinction at best, Louisa."
    a. impressive   **b.** questionable   **c.** local   **d.** unrivaled

Vocabulary Worksheet 1 *(cont.)*

Wish You Well

13. "What's your name?" she asked.

"Billy Davis," he said proudly.

"Are you always that *scintillating*, Billy Davis?"

a. witty   **b.** ill-mannered   **c.** scatter-brained   **d.** conceited

14. She grabbed Billy by his overall straps and threw him to the dirt, where he lay stunned, probably both at her strength and at her *audacity*.

a. speed   **b.** fury   **c.** boldness   **d.** effectiveness

15. There were *corpulent* gray clouds loitering about from a passed storm, their underbellies outlined in flaming reddish-pink.

a. long   **b.** pale   **c.** flat   **d.** fat

B. Read carefully the definition of each word. Then, write a sentence of your own using that word. Include in your sentences clues to the meanings of the defined words.

16. rejuvenated *v.:* made to feel or seem young again; made new or fresh

_____

_____

17. sonorous *adj.:* rich and full of sound; deep

_____

_____

18. eclectic *adj.:* diverse; made up of material from many different sources or systems

_____

_____

19. feigned *v.:* pretended

_____

_____

20. meticulously *adv.:* extremely carefully; with great attention to detail

_____

_____

Name _____ Date _____

Vocabulary Worksheet 2

Wish You Well

A. Circle the letter of the word or phrase that most nearly defines the italicized word in each excerpt from *Wish You Well*.

1. She stretched, *gingerly* touched the floor, and went to look out the window.
   a. cautiously   **b.** enthusiastically   **c.** sleepily   **d.** quietly

2. They fought many pitched battles with flying monkeys and melting witches, and with a little *ingenuity* and some luck at just the right moments, good always triumphed over evil on the glorious Virginia mountain.
   a. bravery   **b.** deceit   **c.** exertion   **d.** cleverness

3. And the *exuberant* mayor threw his straw boater hat high into the air. And the crowd joined him in the cheer, and more hats were catapulted into the swirling breeze.
   a. reluctant   **b.** departing   **c.** high-spirited   **d.** re-elected

4. "Gee, that's about as exciting as watching somebody sleep," was Lou's *considered* opinion.
   a. sarcastic   **b.** spur-of-the-moment   **c.** thought out   **d.** humorous

5. Later, she watched Cotton drive off, while Oz and Lou playfully chased his convertible down the road, and Eugene *diligently* worked on some farm equipment.
   a. sadly   **b.** busily   **c.** distractedly   **d.** noisily

6. However, it seemed they were all doomed to hell according to this fleshy Baptist minister. Jesus had given his life for them, and a sorry lot they were, he said, himself included. Not good for much other than sinning and similar *lax* ways.
   a. spiritually false   **b.** inconsiderate   **c.** arrogant   **d.** morally loose

7. Oz had brought his ball and gloves to the church supper, and he threw with Lou and then with some of the other boys. The men gawked at his *prowess* and said Oz had an arm like they had never seen before.
   a. superior skill   **b.** fastball   **c.** unflagging energy   **d.** stance

8. 'But it is so beautiful here,' the preacher replied. 'Think of the wretched of the city living in *squalor*. How can a man of the open air and the fine earth say such a thing?'
   a. crowded conditions   **b.** artificial environments   **c.** extreme misery   **d.** noisy conditions

9. The throaty growls and *ominous* thrashing of underbrush were close upon them.
   a. catlike   **b.** threatening   **c.** powerful   **d.** periodic

10. The men and women walking the streets were very few in number, and their faces carried an anxious *pallor*.
    a. lack of expression   **b.** look of weariness   **c.** look of embarrassment   **d.** lack of color

11. " . . . Lives of great men all remind us / We can make our lives *sublime*, /And, departing, leave behind us . . . Footprints on the sands of time."
    a. momentary   **b.** agreeable   **c.** famous   **d.** inspiring

Vocabulary Worksheet 2 *(cont.)*

Wish You Well

12. He stopped when he saw Miller and another man there, who was tall, *portly,* and very well dressed, his fine silver hair combed neatly on a head so massive it seemed hardly natural.

    a. middle-aged   **b.** heavy   **c.** handsome   **d.** relaxed

13. Goode continued, "In order to fully protect Miss Cardinal's rights in this matter, we are seeking to have her declared mentally unfit…so that an orderly disposition of her affairs may be conducted, including this very *lucrative* offer from Southern Valley."

    a. well-paying   **b.** crafty   **c.** businesslike   **d.** trustworthy

14. Cotton went and stood over near the jury. "So, she sounds like a woman of *indomitable* spirit. . . ."

    a. level-headed   **b.** narrow-minded   **c.** unsuitable   **d.** unconquerable

15. The man said nothing in response but merely drifted back to his table like an *errant* cloud and collapsed in his chair.

    a. airy   **b.** stray   **c.** thunderous   **d.** bulging

B. Read carefully the definition of each word. Then, write a sentence of your own using that word. If possible, include in your sentences clues to the meanings of the defined words.

16. unbridled *adj.:* free from any restraint; uncontrolled

_____

_____

17. luminous *adj.:* glowing

_____

_____

18. circumvent *v.:* to go around; to thwart

_____

_____

19. propensity *n.:* natural disposition; tendency

_____

_____

20. conducive *adj.:* that contributes or leads to

_____

_____

Writing About the Novel

LETTER WRITING

Amanda's News

The bundle of letters that Amanda has written to Louisa over the years figures prominently in *Wish You Well*. Lou reads one of the letters to Oz at the end of chapter 28. What news might Amanda have reported to Louisa in the other letters? Look through the book for clues to the Cardinals' daily life before they moved to the mountain. Then, write four letters from Amanda to Louisa reporting both everyday and significant events.
(Creative Writing)

PERSUASION AND DEBATE

Just Rewards?

Some readers enjoy the feel-good quality of *Wish You Well*'s ending. Others are of the opinion that the resolution and epilogue go too far in rewarding the characters and are unrealistic. With whom do you agree? Does *Wish You Well* resolve its plot fairly and enjoyably, or is it too neat and optimistic to be believable? Write a one-page statement of your opinion. If another classmate is interested, have her or him write a statement as well, and hold a debate. Make a copy of your statement, and exchange statements with your opponent. During the debate, present your statement and rebut your opponent's. Allow the class to determine the winner.
(Critical Writing)

COMPARE AND CONTRAST

Finches and Cardinals

Read Harper Lee's novel *To Kill a Mockingbird*, about a young girl named Scout Finch growing up in a southern town that becomes divided over a court case. Then, write four or five paragraphs in which you do the following:

- Briefly summarize *To Kill a Mockingbird*.
- Explain how it is similar to *Wish You Well*.
- Explain how it is different from *Wish You Well*.
- Explain what Scout and Louisa have in common and what makes them different.

Share your conclusions with the class in a presentation based on your writing.
(Critical Writing)

OBITUARY

A Writer's Life

Because Jack Cardinal was an important, critically acclaimed writer, most important newspapers would have printed an obituary after his untimely death. Review what the novel says about Jack, paying attention to his upbringing, education, professional life, and accomplishments. Then, write an obituary that gives an overview of Jack Cardinal's life and work.
(Creative Writing)

POEMS

Mountain Words

Review the dialect of the native inhabitants of Louisa's mountain and the nearby towns. Then, using this dialect, compose a poem that addresses an important event in the novel or describes an aspect of the landscape. Consider one of the following:

- Diamond's death
- the barn fire
- Lou and Oz's first sight of the farm
- the final day of the trial

Next, rewrite your poem in standard English. Write a paragraph comparing the two poems. Which better captures the mood of the novel? Which makes the scene come alive more?
(Creative/Critical Writing)

Cross-Curricular Connections

SOCIAL STUDIES

Resources Resource

Natural resource industries such as coal, petroleum, and lumber are important to the economy and culture of the characters in *Wish You Well*. Choose one of these industries to research, focusing on its effect on the economy and culture of Virginia. Write a two-to-four-paragraph encyclopedia entry on the industry and its relationship to Virginia. Conclude your entry with a list of two or three sources (books, articles, or Web sites) that a reader might consult to learn more on the subject.

SCIENCE

Unconscious Accuracy

How realistic is Amanda's incapacitation? Do research at the library and on the Internet to find out about comas and other kinds of prolonged unconsciousness. Create a chart detailing their causes and symptoms and comparing them to Amanda's condition. Sum up your findings in a paragraph or two explaining what, if any, real-life condition Amanda probably has.

GEOGRAPHY

Mountain Map

Most of *Wish You Well* takes place in the mountains of southwestern Virginia. Research the geography of this area and create a map of the region. Label points of interest such as high mountains, major rivers, and towns. Attach to the map information about the land, its features, and its climate. Present your map to the class and explain its features.

DRAMA

High-Speed Drama

A great deal happens in *Wish You Well*, but the really crucial events are relatively rare. With a small group, pick out only those events that are most important for an understanding of the plot of the story. Then, pare down each of those scenes to the bare minimum dialogue and action necessary for an understanding of the scene, paraphrasing dialogue and inserting asides, if necessary. Set these scenes down in a script, and assign parts. If you do not have enough group members to cover all the parts, have actors take multiple parts, using hats or wigs to signal character changes. Keep rehearsing the play until you can perform it in five minutes or less. Then, perform your play for the class.

ART

What It's Like to Be Lou

For the most part, the events of *Wish You Well* are seen through the eyes of Lou, a twelve-year-old girl. Give life to Lou's perceptions in a series of four illustrations. Find the most important moment for Lou in each of the four chapter divisions of the novel (1–10, 11–20, 21–30, 31–Epilogue). For each, create an illustration that shows the scene from Lou's point of view, both physically and emotionally. Try to capture the details of the scene's location and also express Lou's feelings about the location at that time. Use any materials you like, but choose shapes, colors, and textures that reflect Lou's mood. Display your illustrations for the class.

Multimedia and Internet Connections

NOTE: Check with your teacher about school policies on accessing Internet sites.

TELEVISION: NEWS REPORT

Court Report

With a group of classmates, videotape a news report on the final day of the court battle for control of Louisa's property. Assign members of the group roles as each of the key characters in the scene. Assign one group member the role of reporter to supply background and commentary on the proceedings. Show the finished report to the class.

INTERNET: WEB SITE

Wish You Well on the World Wide Web

Plan a Web site devoted to *Wish You Well*. Begin with a home page explaining the purpose of the Web site and describing *Wish You Well*. The site should include various areas with information and images related to *Wish You Well*. Here are some suggestions:

- biographical information on David Baldacci
- reports by you and your classmates on the book
- background information on the Appalachians and southwestern Virginia
- links to other sites dealing with *Wish You Well*, Baldacci, Virginia, or the Appalachians

If possible, take your plan to the next level and create your Web site on the Internet.

PERFORMANCE: VIDEO

Picture Show

With two or three other students, plan and videotape a scene as if it were a segment of a movie version of *Wish You Well*. First, discuss and decide each character's behavior, motives, and attitude in that scene. Then, plan your sets, props, costumes, sound effects, and music (if another student in your class is doing the composition activity on this page, you might collaborate with him or her on the music for your scene). Convert the scene into a script, including stage directions. With one group member as the director and another as the cameraperson, videotape the scene. Show your videotape to the class.

COMPOSITION: MUSIC

The Music of the Mountain

Imagine that you are a composer and have been hired to write the music for a film version of *Wish You Well*. Compose the background music for a favorite scene, tailoring the composition to the tone and mood of the scene (if other students in your class are doing the performance activity on this page, you might collaborate with them). The tone or mood of the music can be altered by making it faster or slower, by changing to another key, or by changing instruments. Play your music or a recording of it for the class. Then explain or demonstrate how the music might be interpreted to suggest the tone or mood of the scene.

AUDIOTAPE: RADIO INTERVIEW

Another Point of View

With a partner, develop a radio interview with a character other than Lou from *Wish You Well*. The person playing the interviewer should carefully develop a series of questions beforehand, and the person playing the interviewee should research his or her character beforehand. You may want to rehearse the interview once or twice before you finalize it. Record the interview on audiotape, and play it for the class.

Introducing the Connections

The **Connections** that follow this novel in the HRW Library edition create the opportunity for students to relate the book's themes to other genres, times, and places and to their own lives. The following chart will facilitate your use of these additional works. Succeeding pages offer **Making Meanings** questions to stimulate student response.

Selection	Summary, Connection to Novel
from **Lucy** Jamaica Kincaid *Novel excerpt*	This novel tells the story of Lucy, a nineteen-year-old young woman who leaves her home in Antigua to work as a nanny in America. Like Lou and Oz, Lucy is forced to adjust to a strange, new environment.
from **Growing Up** Russell Baker *Memoir excerpt*	Like Lou and Oz, Russell Baker lost his father when he was a child. Baker, who was just five at the time—a little younger than Oz—went with his mother to live in the rural mountains of Virginia, the land of Baker's ancestors. The events in this excerpt take place during the 1930s, the years of the Great Depression, about ten years earlier than the events in *Wish You Well*.
Mystic Waters Steenie Harvey *Article*	Wishing wells are an important part of *Wish You Well*. This article gives a brief history of wishing wells in Ireland, where the wells are thought, traditionally, to have great power to benefit people's lives.
from **Christy** Catherine Marshall *Novel excerpt*	Based on the real-life experiences of Catherine Marshall's mother, *Christy* relates the story of a young woman who leaves her home to work as a teacher up in the mountains of Appalachia. Unlike Lou and Oz, Christy leaves her home voluntarily. But like them, she struggles to adapt to her new surroundings.

Exploring the Connections

Making Meanings

from *Lucy*

Connecting with the Novel

How is Lucy's experience different from that of Lou and Oz Cardinal? How is it similar?

1. Lucy sleeps soundly on her first night in her new home. Is this because she is happy?

2. What is Lucy's job?

3. How does Kincaid develop an **atmosphere** (a mood or feeling created in a piece of writing) with certain details? Identify the details.

READING CHECK

a. What time of year is it when Lucy arrives in her new home?

b. Where does Lucy come from?

from *Growing Up*

Connecting with the Novel

Compare the personalities of Baker's grandmother Ida Rebecca and the Cardinals' great-grandmother Louisa.

1. Do you think Ida Rebecca was a good mother? Explain why or why not.

2. What elements of this story make it humorous?

3. Describe Ida Rebecca's initial impressions of Baker's mother.

4. Why do you think Baker says that his father's decision to defy Ida Rebecca with a marriage she hated may have been "the bravest act of his life"?

READING CHECK

a. When did the Baker family settle in the region?

b. What was Daniel Baker's profession?

c. Who was the author's father?

Making Meanings

Mystic Waters

Connecting with the Novel

What similarities can you find between the wishing well in *Wish You Well* and those described in "Mystic Waters"?

1. What did the early Christian missionaries do in order to gain more converts to Christianity?

2. Irony is the discrepancy between expectation and reality. How is the pilgrimage to St. Lazair's Well an example of irony?

3. Why do you think people still visit wells in the hope of a cure or a miracle?

READING CHECK

a. Approximately how many wells are there in Ireland?

b. What is the Gaelic name for *well*?

c. Who were the Druids?

from Christy

Connecting with the Novel

Lou, Oz, and Christy leave their homes to live in a new and strange place. How do they each feel about this dramatic change in their lives?

1. In this excerpt, what details show that Christy is eager for others to accept her as an adult?

2. How do Christy's parents feel about her decision to leave home to teach in an isolated mountain community?

3. What element of the old doctor's description of the people in the Appalachians most shocks and affects Christy?

READING CHECK

a. Is this the first time Christy has left her hometown?

b. Where did Christy learn about the school in Cutter Gap?

Name _____ Date _____

TEST PART I: OBJECTIVE QUESTIONS

In the space provided, mark each true statement _T_ and each false statement _F._
(10 points)

_____ **1.** The death of Lou's father makes her all the more appreciative of her mother.

_____ **2.** Amanda's condition is largely mental.

_____ **3.** Diamond lives on Louisa's farm.

_____ **4.** Because of George Davis's behavior, Louisa will have nothing to do with the Davis family.

_____ **5.** Eugene and the children rebuild the barn by themselves after it burns down.

Complete each statement by writing the letter of the _best_ answer in the space
provided. _(20 points)_

6. Lou's father is an author whose books _____.
   a. are liked by critics and sell well   **c.** are liked by critics but sell poorly
   b. are disliked by critics but sell well

7. Oz uses his necklace to _____.
   a. make Lou feel better   **c.** bargain with the nurse
   b. try to heal his mother

8. When the children run across George Davis while they are out at night, Davis _____.
   a. threatens them with a shotgun   **c.** tells them about the wishing well
   b. helps them find their way home

9. To make a wish at the wishing well, one must leave _____.
   a. money   **c.** a treasured possession
   b. a written request

10. Diamond holds a grudge against Southern Valley Coal and Gas because it _____.
   a. pressured him to leave his land   **c.** burned down his barn
   b. did not take responsibility for his father's death

11. When Lou visits the Davis family, she discovers that they are starving _____.
   a. because the farm is failing   **c.** because they have no tractor
   b. although the farm is prosperous

12. Diamond dies when he _____.
   a. falls into the wishing well   **c.** is shot by George Davis
   b. runs into a coal mine after Jeb

13. When Louisa refuses to sell her property to Southern Valley, _____.
   a. her neighbors are angry and insistent   **c.** George Davis is sympathetic and supportive
   b. her family feels confused and betrayed

TEST   PART I: OBJECTIVE QUESTIONS *(cont.)*

14. The children change their wish at the wishing well from a wish for Amanda's recovery _____.

    a. to a wish for a victory in court

    b. to a wish for Louisa's recovery

    c. to a wish for a successful harvest

15. The children's living situation is resolved when _____.

    a. Louisa recovers

    b. Amanda recovers

    c. Cotton wins the case

TEST PART II: SHORT-ANSWER QUESTIONS

Answer each question, using the lines provided. (40 points)

16. Briefly explain why Lou, Oz, and Amanda move in with Louisa.

_____

_____

_____

17. What new living conditions do Lou and Oz have to adapt to on the farm?

_____

_____

_____

18. What does Eugene share in common with Lou and Oz?

_____

_____

_____

19. How does George Davis respond when Jeb accidentally destroys his still?

_____

_____

_____

20. What is George Davis doing while his child is being born? What character trait does this incident emphasize?

_____

_____

_____

TEST  **PART II: SHORT-ANSWER QUESTIONS** *(cont.)*

21. Why does Southern Valley want to buy Louisa's property, and why will Southern Valley not just buy the mineral rights?

_____

_____

_____

22. What is happening when Louisa suffers her stroke?

_____

_____

_____

23. How does Louisa's stroke help Southern Valley in its attempts to get her land?

_____

_____

_____

24. What do the children leave at the wishing well when they change their wish?

_____

_____

_____

25. What is Cotton suggesting when he asks Commonwealth's attorney Goode "whether Southern Valley has made a donation to your campaign, sir?"

_____

_____

_____

TEST PART III: ESSAY QUESTIONS

Choose *two* of the following topics. Use your own paper to write two or three paragraphs about each topic you choose. (30 points)

1. One **theme** of *Wish You Well* is "Children without Parents." Choose two characters from the book who lack parents or parental guidance. How does their situation affect their actions and feelings? How does one's reaction differ from the other's? In your explanation, give examples from the novel to support your ideas.

2. The main **setting** of *Wish You Well* is the mountain on which Louisa's farm sits. Describe this setting and its effects on the main characters, and explain how the setting helps to shape the main **conflicts** in the story.

3. Identify one of the novel's main **symbols** and explain what it represents. Consider how its meaning changes over the course of the novel and what drives that change. Support your argument with evidence from the novel.

4. One critic says of *Wish You Well,* "The denouement may be too tidy, but readers won't object." Do you agree with this assessment? Are the loose ends tied up in too tidy a fashion? If so, are readers likely to overlook the matter? Why or why not? Support your opinion with evidence from the novel.

5. Discuss how one of the Connections from the back of the novel (HRW LIBRARY edition) is related to a theme, issue, or character in *Wish You Well.*

Use this space to make notes.

Answer Key

Answer Key

Chapters 1–10

■ Making Meanings

> **READING CHECK**
>
> **a.** Their father was killed and their mother incapacitated in a car wreck. Their great-grandmother will look after them.
>
> **b.** Even though she is physically healed, she cannot move or speak.
>
> **c.** He uses what he believes is a magic necklace.
>
> **d.** The house lacks electricity, a telephone, and indoor plumbing.
>
> **e.** Men have been looking around a local man's property and asking questions about coal mines.
>
> **f.** Louisa took him in when he was orphaned as a child.

1. Answers will vary. Some students may mention the death of their father; others may mention the incapacitation of their mother. Others may mention their removal to a new environment.

2. Most students will probably feel that Louisa is a good, caring person because she is willing to take in Eugene, Oz, Lou, and Amanda simply because they need her. Some may mention that she is also stern and stubborn, citing her treatment of the nurse.

3. Lou blames Amanda for her father's death and claims that Amanda deserves her illness.

4. Answers will vary. Students may note that Louisa understands that Oz needs the comfort the necklace provides. Others may respond that underneath her skepticism, Lou wants to believe in the necklace too.

5. Louisa demands that the nurse leaves, even to the point of threatening her with gunfire. She welcomes Amanda and the children and tries to make them feel at home. The difference probably exists because Louisa sees the family as people who need her and the nurse as someone who will interfere with their healing process.

6. Lou aspires to be a writer like her father. Staying in a room with the desk he used to write on provides her an important connection to her father.

7. Answers will vary. Students might mention Odysseus' trek home in the *Odyssey*, the Joads' journey to California in *The Grapes of Wrath*, or Frodo's trip to Mordor in *The Lord of the Rings*.

8. Answers will vary. Students might mention that people like the attention they get for passing on an interesting story. Others might claim that people spread rumors in order to discredit those they fear or dislike.

9. Answers will vary. Some students will claim that the unorthodox English improves the reading experience by bringing the characters' dialect to life. Others may complain that it is excessive and makes reading through dialogue a confusing chore, as each sentence must be puzzled out word by word.

Reading Strategies Worksheet

■ Understanding Characterization

Students' answers will vary. Sample answers are provided.

Lou's mother lives through a car accident that kills her father.
Lou's reaction: Lou blames and resents her mother for her father's death.
Character trait: Lou's attachment to her father causes her to react irrationally to his death.

Oz tries to heal Amanda on the train.
Lou's reaction: She ridicules Oz and tries to get him to stop.
Character trait: Lou tries to be tough-minded and without superstition.

Diamond makes fun of Oz's teddy bear.

Lou's reaction: Lou defends Oz.

Character trait: Lou feels protective of her little brother.

FOLLOW-UP

Answers will vary. Successful paragraphs will most likely predict a resistance to helping her mother heal and conflicts with those who threaten Lou.

Chapters 11–20

■ Making Meanings

> **READING CHECK**
>
> **a.** They are looking for a haunted well.
>
> **b.** He keeps a still in the area, and he wants no one to find it.
>
> **c.** The wisher has to leave a prized possession at the well.
>
> **d.** She gives Lou a stack of letters that Amanda had written to Louisa over the years.
>
> **e.** Lou is ridiculed by the other children and gets into a fight with a boy named Billy Davis.
>
> **f.** They wish for Amanda's recovery.

1. Answers will vary. Some students may claim that her actions are justified by Billy's provocation. Others may point out that Billy does not physically threaten Lou or Oz until Lou attacks him.

2. George Davis is running an illegal still, and is willing to threaten children with a gun to protect it. He is a selfish, contemptible character.

3. Lou feels that such acts are futile, believing that her mother is unreachable and will not recover.

4. The wishing well symbolizes their hope that their mother will recover.

5. The children are discriminated against for being from the mountain rather than from town.

6. Many of his customers are unable to pay him in cash, so he accepts goods as a substitute.

7. Diamond is unsurprised because he put the manure in the car.

8. Answers are personal and need not be shared.

9. Answers will vary. Some students will agree with the comparison, noting that human history is full of examples, such as westward expansion or immigration. Others may disagree, claiming that people are often afraid of change even if it is beneficial; examples may include people who never leave their dying hometowns or stifling jobs.

10. Answers will vary. Some students will complain that it is too much of a coincidence. Others may argue that because Jack Cardinal is supposed to have been such a fine writer and Cotton is such an appreciator of the written word, it is not too great a stretch to imagine that Jack is his favorite author.

Reading Strategies Worksheet

■ Comparing and Contrasting

Students' answers will vary. Sample answers are provided.

Likenesses: wish for their mother's recovery; work hard; intelligent; enjoy Diamond's company

Lou: strong; physically brave; realistic; resists hope

Oz: weak; physically timid; superstitious; feeds his hopes

FOLLOW-UP

Students' paragraphs will vary but should be supported with details from the diagram.

Chapters 21–30

■ Making Meanings

READING CHECK

a. Billy and Lou have had another fight.

b. While the children were out with Diamond and Jeb, Jeb chased a bear, which ran into Davis's still, destroying it.

c. An explosion set off by Southern Valley caused the avalanche that killed Diamond's father. Southern Valley then refused to pay any compensation for the death.

d. She and Louisa go there to help deliver a baby.

e. Davis's home is neglected and full of ill-clothed, starving children. His farm is prosperous and well tended, boasting new, expensive machinery.

f. He is trying to rescue Jeb, who has run into the mine, where Eugene has lit a stick of dynamite.

g. They share some of it with the Davises and sell some of it at a lumber camp.

1. Answers will vary. Those who are surprised may claim that it seems unnatural for a prosperous man to let his family starve. Those who are not surprised may note that Davis is thoroughly villainous in every scene in which he appears, so the way he treats his family seems a logical extension of his previous behavior in the book.

2. Answers will vary. Most students will probably express the opinion that Cotton thinks that the beautiful scene will stir Amanda to wakefulness.

3. No matter her feelings about George Davis, Louisa understands that the other members of his family are victims who need assistance.

4. She moves from contempt and animosity to understanding and sympathy.

5. Up to this point, Oz has been willing to try any supernatural or superstitious cure for his mother. His refusal of this one may signal that he is giving up hope.

6. Diamond has spent his short life in a feud with a mining company that killed his father with a mining explosion, and Diamond himself is killed in a mining explosion.

7. In these chapters, we learn that both Diamond and Jack Cardinal grew up without parents. It could also be argued that Billy Davis's extreme neglect renders him practically parentless.

8. Answers will vary. Possible events include parades sponsored by department stores, sports events sponsored by shoe companies, and concerts sponsored by soft-drink companies. Some students may feel that sponsorship permits events greater funds, thereby allowing them to be more spectacular and reach a wider audience. Others may feel that sponsorship distracts from the proper focus of the event, and lowers the tone of the event.

9. Answers will vary. Examples could include businesses attempting to avoid environmental cleanup or attempting to avoid paying damages for injuries caused by faulty products.

10. Answers will vary. Some students will feel that Davis is too one-dimensional to be believable. Others will claim that his extreme villainy makes him a frightening antagonist.

Reading Strategies Worksheet

■ Summarizing

Students' answers will vary. Sample answers are provided.

George Davis and Louisa are called to the schoolhouse to deal with Billy and Lou's fight.

Jeb destroys George Davis's still.

Cotton takes the family to see the Fourth of July parade in Dickens.

Louisa assists George Davis's wife in childbirth.

Lou reads one of Amanda's old letters to Oz.

Diamond dies in a mine explosion.

FOLLOW-UP

Students' paragraphs will vary but should focus on one event from the diagram and support it with reasons.

Chapters 31–Epilogue

■ Making Meanings

READING CHECK

a. They discover men in hardhats and masks standing around a pipe in the mine floor.

b. Southern Valley Coal and Gas has discovered natural gas in the coal mine on her property.

c. She is incapacitated by a stroke.

d. A group of neighboring farmers shows up with wagons full of materials and helps raise the new barn.

e. He sells all of his books except his Jack Cardinal collection.

f. Miller pushes to have Louisa declared mentally unfit to execute her estate.

g. Amanda revives in the nick of time.

---

1. Answers will vary. Some students will probably be most troubled that Southern Valley Coal and Gas has so much control over the proceedings, others may be most troubled that George Davis is on the jury, and others may be most troubled by the revelation that Southern Valley is responsible for Diamond's death, yet receives no punishment.

2. They visit his treehouse to share out his belongings and visit his grave often.

3. Oz has shown great talent for throwing a ball.

4. The exploration has been going on without her permission.

5. Southern Valley will buy other property only if Louisa agrees to sell; the unpredictability of farming and the loss of job sources in the area have made people desperate to sell their land.

6. If she has given no one power of attorney, then the control of her property is an open question.

7. Answers will vary. Sample answer: Lou and Oz transfer their hope from their mother's recovery to Louisa's, recognizing that they owe her a great debt. Their removal of their old offerings in favor of new ones could be interpreted as giving in to despair regarding their mother's recovery, but the new offerings indicate a hope in Louisa's recovery.

8. The climax occurs when Lou and Oz arrive in the courthouse with Amanda between them. The climax could be seen as ironic because the children have exchanged their wish for Amanda's recovery for a wish for Louisa's recovery, yet Louisa dies and Amanda recovers.

9. Answers will vary. Some students may mention literary figures like Atticus Finch in *To Kill a Mockingbird,* who agrees to represent an unpopular murder-trial defendant because he believes everyone deserves a fair trial. Other students may mention historical figures like Dr. Martin Luther King, Jr., who was a civil rights leader because he believed all people should be treated equally by the law.

10. Answers will vary. Some students will feel that Amanda's recovery is unconvincing, and that a more realistic ending would be more satisfying because it would be a logical consequence of elements of the plot. Other students may feel that the ending is convincing enough, since it does not violate any known laws of the universe, and that a more realistic ending would be less satisfying because it would not reward the main characters enough.

Reading Strategies Worksheet

■ Making Inferences

Students' answers will vary. Sample answers are provided.

Diamond had fallen in love with Lou.

Miller believes that he can get Louisa to change her mind.

Someone has set fire to the barn.

Cotton thinks that Goode is taking the case because he has been bought off by Southern Valley.

Cotton finds the photograph a disgusting ploy.

FOLLOW-UP

Students' answers will vary but should give a valid reason that authors often imply rather than state. Answers should also evaluate Baldacci's skill with this technique and give support for the evaluation.

Literary Elements Worksheets

■ Theme

Answers may vary. Sample answers are provided.

Lou and Oz: father died in car wreck; mother is incapacitated

Diamond: parents died when he was a young child

Eugene: parents died when he was a child

Jack Cardinal: mother abandoned him; father died when he was young

Billy Davis: father abuses him and neglects him to the point of starvation

FOLLOW-UP

Answers will vary, but most students will probably claim that the theme generates readers' sympathy for the characters and provides an important connection between the Cardinal children and their friends and enemies.

■ Symbol

Answers will vary. Sample answers are provided.

THE WISHING WELL

EARLY MEANING

At first, the wishing well stands for Lou and Oz's hope that their mother will recover.

LATER MEANING

Once Louisa has her stroke and the court action to take away her land begins, the children shift the focus of the wishing well away from their mother and onto Louisa. The well then represents their hope for Louisa's recovery.

LOUISA'S LAND

EARLY MEANING

The land's unforgiving beauty makes it a symbol for life: It demands constant toil, but does not promise happiness or plenty.

LATER MEANING

As Southern Valley attempts to gain control of the land, it becomes a symbol of the Cardinal family. If Southern Valley takes the land and destroys it, it will destroy the family as well.

FOLLOW-UP

Answers will vary but should be supported by meaningful reasons.

Vocabulary Worksheets

■ Vocabulary Worksheet 1

A.

1. b.	6. c.	11. d.
2. a.	7. b.	12. b.
3. b.	8. a.	13. a.
4. d.	9. a.	14. c.
5. a.	10. c.	15. d.

B. Answers will vary. Sample answers are provided.

16. **rejuvenated** *v.:* made to feel or seem young again; made new or fresh

   Tired after her long run, Ellen felt *rejuvenated* once she had taken a shower.

17. **sonorous** *adj.:* rich and full of sound; deep

   Tina's favorite radio announcer had a pleasant, *sonorous* voice.

18. **eclectic** *adj.:* diverse; made up of material from many different sources or systems

I had always known that Ed enjoyed foods from many different cultures, but it wasn't until his birthday dinner, with foods from India, China, Peru and Mexico, that I realized how *eclectic* his tastes were.

19. **feigned** *v.:* pretended

Rather than go to the dinner for his cousin Sonia, Tom *feigned* illness, but his act fell apart when Sonia saw him downtown later.

20. **meticulously** *adv.:* extremely carefully; with great attention to detail

The old watch was still running after two hundred years of use, showing how *meticulously* Swiss watchmakers practised their craft in those days.

■ Vocabulary Worksheet 2

A.

1. a.	**6.** d.	**11.** d.
2. d.	**7.** a.	**12.** b.
3. c.	**8.** c.	**13.** a.
4. c.	**9.** b.	**14.** d.
5. b.	**10.** d.	**15.** b.

B. Answers will vary. Sample answers are given.

16. **unbridled** *adj.:* free from any restraint; uncontrolled

Unbridled freedom is not always a good thing because most people need some kind of control over their actions.

17. **luminous** *adj.:* glowing

The alarm clock's *luminous* face makes it easy to see in the dark.

18. **circumvent** *v.:* to go around; to thwart

The speed bumps outside our local SuperMart are useless, because they extend only part of the way across the parking lot. This makes it easy for drivers to *circumvent* them.

19. **propensity** *n.:* natural disposition; tendency

Uncle Chet had such a *propensity* for long rambling stories that one of the more polite nicknames by which he was known was "The Storyteller."

20. **conducive** *adj.:* that contributes or leads to

Hard work is *conducive* to success.

Exploring the Connections

■ *from* Lucy

> **READING CHECK**
> **a.** Lucy arrives in mid-January.
> **b.** She comes from a tropical zone (in fact, the West Indies).

1. She sleeps soundly because she is exhausted from her trip.

2. Lucy takes care of the children during the day and attends school at night.

3. The excerpt is full of vivid details, among them Lucy's new undergarments and the feeling of "newness" they give her; the pale yellowness of the sun; the dream she has of eating with her grandmother; the way people walk quickly in the streets; and so on.

Connecting with the Novel

The main difference is that Lou and Oz are children who are sent to stay with their great-grandmother when their parents are in an accident, whereas Lucy is a young woman who has come to America for her education and professional improvement. On the other hand, both stories deal with young people abruptly uprooted from their familiar surroundings.

Answer Key *(cont.)*

■ *from* Growing Up

> **READING CHECK**
> **a.** They settled there around 1730.
> **b.** He was a gunsmith turned tailor.
> **c.** His father was Benjamin, the eleventh son of Russell's grandparents.

1. Responses will vary. Some students will say she was authoritarian and dictatorial. Others might point out that in such a remote place and time stern authority was what was needed to keep families together.

2. There are several humorous comments in this excerpt, including Baker's description of his grandfather's churchgoing; the number of children born in the Baker family; his grandfather's dying words; and his description of his mother's first meeting with Ida Rebecca.

3. "An overpowering figure accustomed to command." At over six feet in height, Ida Rebecca towered over Baker's mother, and she sat in a commanding position on a high porch.

4. Baker describes his father as a man with little money who nevertheless liked to have a good time. This implies an easygoing personality who would rather not confront someone as forbidding as Ida Rebecca; but in deciding to marry Baker's mother, he stood up to the old lady.

Connecting with the Novel
Ida Rebecca is a much more intimidating personality than Louisa, who treats Lou and Oz with great affection and concern. Also, it is hard to imagine Ida Rebecaa incapacitated in any way, as Louisa is.

■ Mystic Waters

> **READING CHECK**
> **a.** There are three thousand or so wells in Ireland.
> **b.** *Tobar* is the Gaelic name for *well*.
> **c.** They were the priests of the ancient pagan Celtic culture.

1. They incorporated the supposed magic wells into their new religion by transforming them into holy wells rededicated to Christian mystics.

2. The irony is that sufferers from backache are expected to pass beneath a very low flagstone known as the Mass Table. This will almost certainly make the condition worse, not better.

3. Responses will vary. Some students may say that people have always been superstitious. Others may suggest that there are geuine healing properties in some of the wells.

Connecting with the Novel
The well in *Wish You Well* has no mystical history or religious significance, but it shares with the Irish wells—and with all wishing wells—the mysterious property of supposedly granting wishes. Some students may suggest that it apparently does grant wishes.

Answer Key (cont.)

■ *from* Christy

> **READING CHECK**
>
> **a.** This is not the first time she has left home.
>
> **b.** She heard an old doctor talk about the school on the church conference grounds at Montreat. Her family was there for the summer.

1. Christy demonstrates her anxiety by making numerous references to her age. She states that her parents felt she was too young to go off and teach at the school. She thinks that her father jokes with her at the station "as if [she] were nine and not nineteen." She is also embarrassed when she suspects that her father is telling the conductor to take care of her.

2. Christy's parents opposed her decision at first. Christy managed to change their minds, however. At this point in the story, they seem to support her decision.

3. Christy is shocked that a place like the one the doctor described exists so near to her own home. She previously thought that such a place only existed far away from her town, in countries like China or on continents like Africa.

Connecting with the Novel

Lou, Oz, and Christy are going to places they have never seen and know little about. Consequently, they are all a little anxious. Christy, however, seems eager to go and make a difference in a community that needs assistance. Lou is eager to go and see her father's hometown. Oz is less eager and is still clearly recovering from the shock of, in effect, losing both of his parents.

Test

■ Part I: Objective Questions

1. F	**6.** c	**11.** b
2. T	**7.** b	**12.** b
3. F	**8.** a	**13.** a
4. F	**9.** c	**14.** b
5. F	**10.** b	**15.** b

■ Part II: Short-Answer Questions

16. They move in with Louisa because the children's father is killed in the same car wreck that incapacitates Amanda. The children and Amanda have no one else to take care of them.

17. They now have no electricity, indoor plumbing, or telephone. They must get up before dawn to do chores and must walk to and from school.

18. He was also taken in by Louisa when he lacked parents.

19. First he threatens and beats the children. Then, the next day he shows up at Louisa's house, demanding payment.

20. Davis is in the barn helping a mare birth a foal. It emphasizes that Davis finds his property more important than his family.

21. Southern Valley has discovered natural gas in a coal mine on Louisa's property. The company wants to level the mountain and develop the whole area, so it needs the land as well as the rights.

22. Her barn is burning down.

23. With Louisa incapacitated, Southern Valley can push to have her declared incompetent to execute her property.

24. They leave a bundle of letters that Amanda had written to Louisa.

25. Cotton is suggesting that Good has been persuaded to serve the interests of Southern Valley Coal and Gas rather than the interests of the Commonwealth.

■ Part III: Essay Questions

Students should respond to two out of the five essay questions. Answers will vary, but should include specific references to the text.

1. Students should choose to write about two of the following characters: Lou, Oz, Eugene, Diamond, Jack Cardinal, and Billy Davis. Students should explain the effects of the situation on the characters and highlight differences between the two. Evidence from the novel should illustrate the points the students have made about the characters.

2. The mountain is a harsh but beautiful place that requires hard work but promises no rewards. The Cardinals and their allies fall in love with the mountain, but George Davis and Southern Valley Coal and Gas see it as only a resource to exploit. The discovery of natural gas on the mountain leads to a showdown between those who wish to preserve the mountain and those who wish to exploit it.

3. Students will likely choose to write about either the wishing well or Louisa's land. The wishing well changes from a symbol of the children's hope for Amanda's recovery to a symbol of hope for Louisa's recovery. The land changes from a symbol of life to a symbol of family. Evidence from the novel should illustrate both the initial meaning and the shift in meaning.

4. Students should clearly articulate an opinion on whether the denouement is too neat and whether the matter is forgivable. Examples from the novel should illustrate the denouement's success or failure and the book's ability or inability to get the reader to accept the denouement.

5. Responses will vary, but students will probably note in particular the similarities in setting between *Wish You Well* and Baker's memoir *Growing Up,* including the personalities involved and the period (the 1930s and '40s). Lucy's sense of alienation in the excerpt from *Lucy* can be compared to Lou Cardinal's.

Notes

Notes

Notes

Notes

Notes

Notes